David Joy Schon

Applied Mechanics

for Engineers and Technicians

STATICS

Applied Mechanics

for Engineers and Technicians

STATICS

Aldor C. Peterson

Associate Professor of Engineering Mechanics
Iowa State Technical Institute
Iowa State University

ALLYN AND BACON   *BOSTON*

Preface

This text has been prepared primarily for students in technical institutes and similar schools that require a basic knowledge of the principles of mechanics and their application to engineering problems.

The major emphasis is on the application of these principles by use of examples and the solution of a variety of relevant problems; underlying principles are also given considerable attention.

The examples are chosen to illustrate the principles and their applications in a logical, understandable manner. Since this book is intended to serve as an introduction to the subject of statics, the more complex problems have been omitted.

This text may be used by students who have only a knowledge of algebra and the elements of trigonometry or by those who are concurrently taking or have had an introductory course in calculus. A continuity of treatment is provided for either student. Where calculus is used, a noncalculus development is presented first and then a parallel calculus discussion follows directly, set off by a boldface note and rules. Calculus is employed for the derivation of the belt friction equation in Chapter 4 and for the discussion of centroids and moments of inertia in Chapters 5 and 6. The first three chapters contain no calculus.

The use of the free-body diagram is strongly recommended for all problems involving force systems. This is a simple but useful tool contributing greatly to the students' success in the accurate solution of such problems.

ALDOR C. PETERSON

Contents

3 EQUILIBRIUM OF FORCE SYSTEMS   85

4 FRICTION   156

5 CENTROIDS OF AREAS   185

Symbols and Abbreviations

A	force
A	(with subscript) force in direction indicated by subscript
A	area, point
a	area, length, point
α	(alpha) angle
B	force
B	(with subscript) force in direction indicated by subscript
B	point
b	area, length, point
β	(beta) angle
C	force
C	(with subscript) force in direction indicated by subscript
C	couple
C	(with subscript) couple about axis indicated by subscript
C	compressive force
C	point, centroid
c	area, length, point
cos	cosine (of angle)
D	force
D	(with subscript) force in direction indicated by subscript
D	point
d	length, point
d	(e.g., dx, $d\theta$) differential of distance or angle
E	point
Eq.	equation

e	base for natural logarithm (approx. 2.72)
F	force
F	(with subscript) force in direction indicated by subscript
F	point
F'	force of limiting friction
Fig.	figure
ft	foot
ft-lb	foot-pound
G	mass center, point
H	point
h	length
I	rectangular moment of inertia
I	(with subscript) moment of inertia about axis indicated by subscript
in.	inch
in-lb	inch-pound
J_o	polar moment of inertia
K	radius of gyration
K	(with subscript) radius of gyration about axis indicated by subscript
kip	kilopound (1000 lb)
L	length
lb	pound
log	logarithm (common)
ln	logarithm (natural)
M	moment of a force
M	(with subscript) moment about axis or point indicated by subscript
M	(subscript-point and direction) moment about axis passing through point as indicated by subscript
μ	(mu) coefficient of friction
N	normal force
O, o	point, origin of coordinates
P, P'	force
P	(with subscript) force in direction indicated by subscript
π	pi (3.1416)
Q, Q'	force
Q	(with subscript) force in direction indicated by subscript
q	length
R	force, resultant force, reaction force
R	(with subscript) force in direction indicated by subscript
R, r	length, radius
S	force
s	element of area
sq	square
sin	sine (of angle)

Σ	summation
$\mathbf{T}$	force, tensile force
T	time
$\mathbf{T}_S$	smaller tensile force on belt
$\mathbf{T}_L$	larger tensile force on belt
tan	tangent (of angle)
θ	(theta) angle
$\mathbf{U}$	force
V	volume
W	weight
x, y, z	rectangular coordinates
$\bar{x}, \bar{y}, \bar{z}$	rectangular coordinates of centroid, of resultant force
⟶▶	vector representing resultant force
⟹	vector representing moment of force

1

Fundamental Concepts
and Definitions

1-1 INTRODUCTION

Engineering mechanics is a study of forces, and the effects of forces on the bodies upon which they act.

Applied engineering mechanics emphasizes the application of the principles of mechanics to the solution of engineering problems.

Mechanics includes two main branches of study, namely, statics and dynamics. *Statics is that branch of mechanics which deals with the external effects of balanced forces on bodies at rest or moving with uniform motion.* The external effect of a force on a body is either to develop resisting forces, usually called reactions, on the body, or to accelerate the body. When the force system is not balanced and has a resultant not equal to zero, the body will be accelerated and the problem is one of dynamics. When one considers the internal effect of a force on a body, which results in stresses in and change of shape of the body, the problem becomes one of strength of materials. Only problems of statics are considered in this text.

The external effects of a force system on a physical body usually are not changed to a great extent by small changes in shape of the body.

For this reason, bodies in this text are assumed to be rigid bodies. *A rigid body is one in which all particles remain at fixed distances from each other.*

1-2 FORCES

A force is the action of one body on another body which changes or tends to change the motion of the body acted on. Because of the inertia of all material bodies, the body acted on will react to or oppose the force acting on it with a force of equal màgnitude and opposite sense (according to Newton's third law of motion). Thus forces always exist in pairs: there is a simultaneous action—equal, opposite, and collinear (along the same straight line)—of two bodies, each acting on the other, either in contact (as is generally the case) or at a distance (as with the gravitational pull of the earth). However, in the analysis of statics problems, usually only one of the two equal and opposite forces (one of the pair) is considered: the effect of one body acting on the other.

1-3 CHARACTERISTICS OF A FORCE

In order to determine a force completely, its three properties, called *characteristics*, must be specified: (1) *its magnitude*, (2) *the location of a point on its line of action*, and (3) *its direction (sense and slope)*. These properties of a force determine its external effect on a body.

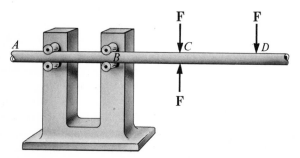

Fig. 1-1

A change in any one of these characteristics will cause a change in the external effect of the force on the body upon which it acts. For example, suppose a force **F** is acting down at point *C* of Fig. 1-1. The reaction at *B* will be upward because of the lower roller acting against the beam *AD*. Also, if the magnitude of the force **F** is changed to 0.5*F*, the reaction at *B* will be less. Now, if the direction of the force **F** is changed to upward, the reaction at B will change to a downward force because of the top roller at B bearing against the beam AD. Finally, if the force F is moved to point D, the reaction at B will be increased. Thus it is seen that a change of any one of the characteristics of a force will cause a change in the reactions (external effects) on the body.

1-4 SCALAR AND VECTOR QUANTITIES

Quantities which possess magnitude only are called scalar quantities. Examples are mass, volume, work, and time. *A vector quantity is represented by a directed scaled line which shows direction as well as magnitude.* The direction is indicated by an arrow at one end of the line and the magnitude of the quantity by the scaled length of the line. Examples are force, velocity, acceleration, impulse, and momentum.

In this book, in order to distinguish clearly between vectors and scalars, letters representing *magnitudes* of vectors and other scalar quantities are set in lightface type, while letters representing vector quantities are set in **boldface** type.

Vector quantities can be classified as free or as localized vectors. *A free vector is one which has a specified direction but does not act through any particular point. A localized vector has a specific line of action or a particular point through which it must pass.*

1-5 TRANSMISSIBILITY OF A FORCE

The principle of transmissibility states that the external effects of a force are independent of the point of application of the force along its line of action. Only the external effects on the body remain unchanged however. The internal effects may vary greatly as the force is moved along its line of action.

For example, suppose the two equal, opposite, and collinear forces **P** and **Q** are acting on the body shown in Fig. 1-2a at points A and B respectively. Under the action of these forces the body is in compression.

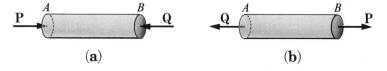

$$(a) \qquad\qquad\qquad (b)$$

Fig. 1-2

If force **P** is moved along its line of action to *B*, and **Q** is moved to *A*, as shown in Fig. 1–2b, the body is in tension. Thus the internal effect on the body is changed. However the body is in equilibrium before and after the forces are translated, and therefore the external effect is not changed.

1-6 CLASSIFICATION OF FORCES

Any number of forces, considered as a group, constitute a force system. If the action lines of all the forces intersect in a common point, the force system is said to be *concurrent*, and if the action lines do not intersect at a common point, it is *nonconcurrent*. When all the forces lie in the same plane, the force system is *coplanar*, and when the forces do not lie in the same plane, *noncoplanar*. A *parallel* force system is one in which the action lines of the forces are parallel, and a *nonparallel* system is one in which the action lines are not parallel. When the forces of a system have a common action line, the system is *collinear*.

1-7 COMPOSITION OF FORCES

The process of reducing a force system to the simplest force system possible, namely the *resultant*, that has the same external effect on a body as the original force system *is called composition.* The parallelogram law is the fundamental concept on which the composition of forces is based.

The parallelogram law may be stated as follows: The resultant of two intersecting forces is the vector diagonal of a parallelogram whose sides are the vectors of those two forces. Note that the resultant passes through the point of intersection of the two forces.

The parallelogram law is illustrated in Fig. 1–3a. The resultant of the two forces **P** and **Q** is the single force **R**, which passes through point

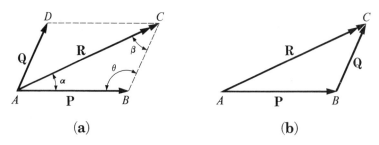

(a)   (b)

Fig. 1-3

A, the point of concurrence of **P** and **Q**. The magnitude of the resultant force **R** is determined graphically by drawing the parallelogram to scale, so that the length of each force vector in the parallelogram represents its magnitude.

The magnitude of the resultant also can be found algebraically by using the cosine law for a triangle. In the parallelogram formed by forces **P** and **Q** the side *BC* is parallel and equal to side *AD* (**Q**). Thus, referring to triangle *ABC* in Fig. 1-3a,

$$R = (P^2 + Q^2 - 2PQ \cos \theta)^{1/2}$$

The angle which the resultant makes with either force can be determined by the law of sines as follows:

$$\frac{\sin \alpha}{Q} = \frac{\sin \theta}{R} = \frac{\sin \beta}{P}$$

Although it is not necessary that a parallelogram or triangle of forces be drawn, the student will be greatly assisted in the use of the above equations by such sketches.

When the action lines of the two forces are perpendicular to each other, the above equations reduce to

$$R = (P^2 + Q^2)^{1/2}$$

and

$$\cos \alpha = \frac{P}{R} \qquad \cos \beta = \frac{Q}{R}$$

The triangle law, as a corollary to the parallelogram law, *may be stated as follows: If two forces are represented by their free vectors, placed tip to tail, their resultant vector is the third side of the triangle and the direction of the resultant will be from the tail of the first vector to the tip of the last vector.*

In Fig. 1–3b the resultant **R**, drawn from the tail of the first vector to the tip of the last vector (i.e., from *A* to *C*), has the same magnitude and direction as the diagonal of the parallelogram *ABCD* in Fig. 1–3a, but it does not pass through the point of concurrence of the forces **P** and **Q** and therefore does not have the correct position of the line of action of the resultant. In this case the force **Q** is represented by the free vector **BC**.

Example 1-1 Determine the resultant of two concurrent forces: a 120-lb force acting upward and to the right at an angle of 15° with the horizontal and a 100-lb force acting upward and to the right at an angle of 80° with the horizontal, as shown in Fig. 1-4a.

Solution: Fig. 1-4b shows the two forces intersecting at point *A*. *BC* is drawn equal to and parallel to the 100-lb force, and *DC* is drawn equal to and parallel to the 120-lb force, completing the parallelogram of which **R**, the diagonal, is the resultant.

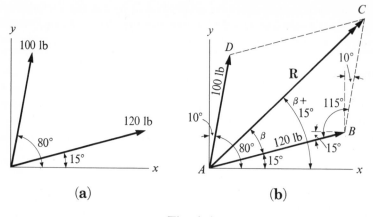

(a)   **(b)**

Fig. 1-4

Angle *ABC* is equal to 15° plus 90° plus 10° and therefore is equal to 115°. Substituting in the cosine law, the magnitude of the resultant is found as follows:

$$R = [120^2 + 100^2 - 2(120)(100) \cos 115°]^{1/2}$$
$$= [14,400 + 10,000 - 24,000(-0.4226)]^{1/2}$$
$$= 186 \text{ lb}$$

The angle between the 120-lb force and the resultant can be determined by using the law of sines as follows:

$$\frac{\sin \beta}{100} = \frac{\sin 115°}{186}$$

$$\sin \beta = \frac{0.9063}{1.86} = 0.5175$$

$$\beta = 31.17°$$

The resultant therefore makes an angle of 15° plus 31.17°, equal to 46.17°, with the horizontal.

1-8 RESOLUTION OF A FORCE

In the preceding section the resultant of two intersecting, or concurrent, forces was found. When these two forces intersect on the line of action of the resultant, the external effect on a body of the resultant and of the two forces is identical. The reverse of this process, namely, finding two components of a force which will have the same external effect on a body as the force itself, is very useful in mechanics. This process, known as the *resolution of a force*, may be accomplished by the use of the parallelogram or triangle law, and the components may be found algebraically or graphically. For most purposes rectangular (mutually perpendicular) components of a force are more useful than oblique (nonrectangular) components. *A rectangular component of a force is equal to the product of the force and the cosine of the angle between the force and the component.* To obtain rectangular components, the parallelogram becomes a rectangle as shown in Fig. 1–5. One pair of rectangular components of **F** (a horizontal and a vertical component) is

$$\mathbf{F}_x = \mathbf{OA} = F \cos \theta \rightarrow$$
$$\mathbf{F}_y = \mathbf{OB} = F \cos \alpha = F \sin \theta \uparrow$$

Note that a complete description of the vector components of the vector **F** includes an indication of their directions, shown by arrows as in the above equations.

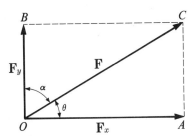

Fig. 1-5

The components of a force must intersect on the action line of the force. Thus, **OA** and **OB** are correct components of **F** since the action line of their resultant passes through point O, their point of intersection. Other pairs of rectangular components may be obtained by varying the angle θ between the force **F** and one of the components.

Often it is necessary to resolve a force in space into three mutually perpendicular components parallel to their coordinate axes. To accomplish this, the force **F** (along AB) in Fig. 1–6 is first resolved into the two components along AC and AD by means of the parallelogram law; and the component along AD is then resolved further into components along AE and AG. From the figure it is found that

$$\mathbf{F}_x = \mathbf{AC} = F \cos \theta_x \rightarrow$$
$$\mathbf{F}_y = \mathbf{AG} = F \cos \theta_y \uparrow$$
$$\mathbf{F}_z = \mathbf{AE} = F \cos \theta_z \nearrow$$

Also, the length of the vector **F** can be expressed in terms of the lengths of the vectors **AC**, **AG**, and **AE** as

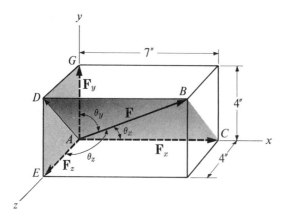

Fig. 1-6

$$F = (AC^2 + AG^2 + AE^2)^{1/2}$$

Therefore the magnitude of the components may be determined as follows:

$$F_x = AC = \frac{\text{length of } AC}{\text{length of } F}(F) = F \cos \theta_x$$

$$F_y = AG = \frac{\text{length of } AG}{\text{length of } F}(F) = F \cos \theta_y$$

$$F_z = AE = \frac{\text{length of } AE}{\text{length of } F}(F) = F \cos \theta_z$$

The angles θ_x, θ_y, and θ_z are the angles between the force **F** and the components of **F** along the coordinate axes. The three components intersect at point A, which is on the line of action of the resultant force.

If nonrectangular components of a force are desired, such as the components **P** and **Q** of force **F** in Fig. 1–7, a convenient method of

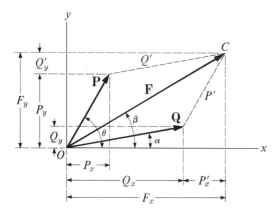

Fig. 1-7

solution is to resolve the force **F** into rectangular components, F_x and
F_y, and then equate each of these rectangular components of **F** to the
sum of the corresponding rectangular components of the forces **P** and **Q**.
Fig. 1–7 illustrates this procedure. In Fig. 1–7, $P'_x = P_x$ and $Q'_y = Q_y$,
since in the parallelogram $P' = P$ and $Q' = Q$. The horizontal distance
from O to C is $F_x = P'_x + Q_x = P_x + Q_x$. That is, the horizontal component of the force **F** is equal to the sum of the horizontal components
of the components **P** and **Q**. Also, the vertical distance from O to C is
$F_y = P_y + Q'_y = P_y + Q_y$. That is, the vertical component of the force
F is equal to the sum of the vertical components of the components
P and **Q**.

Example 1-2 Determine the rectangular components of the 120-lb force in
    Fig. 1-8a, which makes an angle of 30° with the x axis.

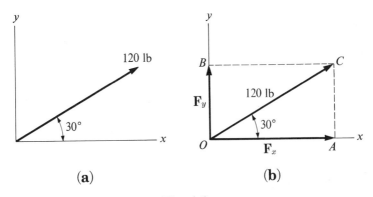

Fig. 1-8

Solution: From the tip of the 120-lb force, drop perpendiculars to the x and y
    axes as shown in Fig. 1-8b, forming a parallelogram of which the 120-lb
    force is the diagonal. Graphically the x component is **OA** and the y com-
    ponent is **OB**. Algebraically the components may be determined as follows:

$$F_x = OA = 120 \cos 30° = 120 \left(\frac{3^{1/2}}{2} \right) = 104 \text{ lb} \rightarrow$$

$$F_y = OB = 120 \cos 60° = 120 \sin 30° = 60 \text{ lb} \uparrow$$

    Note that the components, F_x and F_y, in order to correctly and com-
    pletely represent the action of the 120-lb force, must intersect each other
    on the line of action of the 120-lb force.

Example 1-3 Let the magnitude of the force **F** in Fig. 1-6 equal 180 lb. Deter-
    mine the x, y, and z components of force **F**.

Solution: The length of the diagonal **F** is

$$AB = (4^2 + 4^2 + 7^2)^{1/2} = 9 \text{ in.}$$

and the scale for **F** is $180/9 = 20$ lb per in. Therefore the three components are

$$\mathbf{F}_x = 20(7) = 140 \text{ lb} \rightarrow \text{ through } A$$
$$\mathbf{F}_y = 20(4) = 80 \text{ lb} \uparrow \text{ through } A$$
$$\mathbf{F}_z = 20(4) = 80 \text{ lb} \nearrow \text{ through } A$$

Example 1-4   Let the magnitude of the force **F** in Fig. 1-7 equal 160 lb. Determine the nonrectangular components, **P** and **Q**, of the 160-lb force **F**, if $\theta = 60°$, $\beta = 30°$, and $\alpha = 10°$.

Solution: The rectangular components of the 160-lb force **F** are

$$\mathbf{F}_x = 160 \cos 30° = 160(0.866) = 138.5 \text{ lb} \rightarrow$$
$$\mathbf{F}_y = 160 \sin 30° = 160(0.500) = 80.0 \text{ lb} \uparrow$$

The rectangular components of the nonrectangular components **P** and **Q** are

$$\mathbf{Q}_x = Q \cos 10° = 0.985Q \rightarrow$$
$$\mathbf{Q}_y = Q \sin 10° = 0.174Q \uparrow$$
$$\mathbf{P}_x = P \cos 60° = 0.500P \rightarrow$$
$$\mathbf{P}_y = P \sin 60° = 0.866P \uparrow$$

Equating the rectangular components of the 160-lb force **F** to the algebraic sum of the rectangular components of **P** and **Q** in the x and y directions, respectively, gives

$$0.985Q + 0.500P = 138.5$$
$$0.174Q + 0.866P = 80.0$$

Solving these two equations simultaneously gives

$$Q = 104.7 \text{ lb}$$

$$P = 71.2 \text{ lb}$$

Both nonrectangular components intersect the 160-lb force **F** at a common point.

PROBLEMS

1-1.   Determine a pair of horizontal and vertical components of the 130-lb force in Fig. P 1-1.

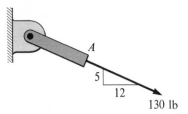

Fig. P 1-1   130 lb

1-2. Determine a pair of horizontal and vertical components of the 300-lb force in Fig. P 1–2.

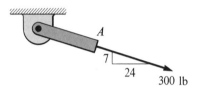

Fig. P 1-2   300 lb

1-3. Determine a pair of horizontal and vertical components of the 600-lb force on the cantilever beam in Fig. P 1–3.

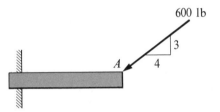

Fig. P 1-3

1-4. A y component of the force **F**, applied to the bracket in Fig. P 1–4, is 100 lb upward. Determine **F** and its corresponding x component.

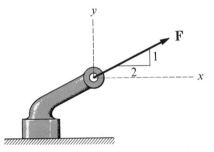

Fig. P 1-4

1-5. **(a)** Can two forces which are the components of the 200-lb force shown in Fig. P 1–5 intersect at B? **(b)** Determine the horizontal and vertical components of the 200-lb force shown in Fig. P 1–5 and completely represent them on a sketch. **(c)** Are each of the two components of a force always less in magnitude than the force?

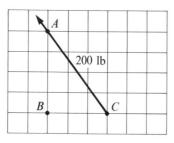

Fig. P 1-5

1-6. **(a)** Determine the horizontal and vertical components of the 400-lb force shown in Fig. P 1–6. **(b)** Determine the components of the 400-lb force shown in Fig. P 1–6 whose action lines are parallel to AC and CB.

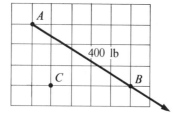

Fig. P 1-6

1-7. Resolve the 1300-lb force in Fig. P 1–7 into two nonrectangular components, one having a line of action along AB and the other parallel to BC.

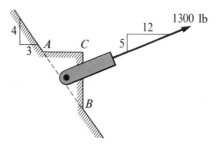

Fig. P 1-7

1-8. Resolve the 200-lb force acting on body ABC in Fig. P 1–8 into two components, one having a line of action through A and the other having a line of action along BC.

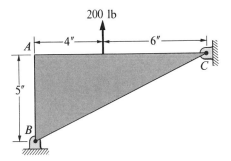

Fig. P 1-8

1-9. Resolve the 100-lb force shown in Fig. P 1–9 into two components, **P** having a line of action through point *A*, and **Q** having a line of action along *bc*.

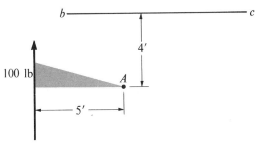

Fig. P 1-9

1-10. Determine the horizontal and vertical components of the 200-lb force shown in Fig. P 1–10 when θ is **(a)** 30°; **(b)** 20°.

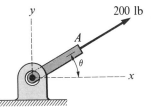

Fig. P 1-10

1-11. Resolve the 130-lb force shown in Fig. P 1–11 into two components, one of the forces **P** having a line of action along the *u*-axis and the other force **Q** having a line of action parallel to the *v*-axis.

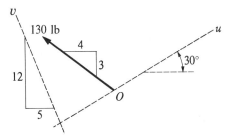

Fig. P 1-11

1-12. For the force system shown in Fig. P 1–12 determine **(a)** the algebraic sum of the horizontal components of the forces of the system, and **(b)** the algebraic sum of the vertical components of the forces of the system.

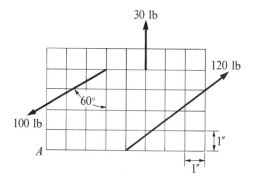

Fig. P 1-12

1-13. Determine a set of three rectangular components of the force **F** shown as the diagonal of the box in Fig. P 1–13 when the magnitude of **F** equals 270 lb.

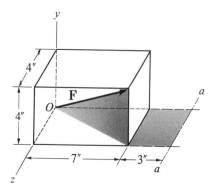

Fig. P 1-13

1-14. Determine the x, y, and z components of the 70-lb force shown in Fig. P 1–14.

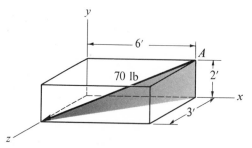

Fig. P 1-14

In Problems 1-15, 1-16, and 1-17 the action line of the given force passes through the origin and the indicated point and is directed from the origin toward the point. The positive directions of the coordinate axes are as shown in Fig. P 1–15. In each problem determine a set of x, y, and z components of the given force.

	Magnitude	Point (x, y, z)		
1-15.	170 lb	9,	8,	12
1-16.	220 lb	−9,	2,	−6
1-17.	263 lb	3,	−6,	7

Fig. P 1-15

1-9 MOMENT OF A FORCE

The moment of a force with respect to a moment axis perpendicular to a plane containing the force is a vector whose magnitude equals the product of the magnitude of the force and the perpendicular distance between the force and the moment axis. The moment vector acts along the moment axis, and the sense of the moment vector is the direction a right-hand screw would advance if turned about the moment axis with the same sense of rotation as the moment of the force. The moment of a force measures its tendency to produce turning with respect to the moment axis. Thus, in Fig. 1–9, the magnitude of the moment of the force **F**, which lies in the xz plane, with respect to the y axis is Fd, and applying the

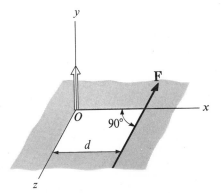

Fig. 1-9

principle of the right-hand screw, the sense of the moment vector whose magnitude is Fd is upward along the y axis. A double-lined open arrow is used to represent a moment vector, as indicated in Fig. 1–9. The magnitude Fd of the moment of the force $\mathbf{F}$ with respect to the y axis is the product of the magnitude of the force $\mathbf{F}$ and the perpendicular distance between $\mathbf{F}$ and the point O where the y axis intersects the plane in which $\mathbf{F}$ lies. Fd can also be expressed as the magnitude of the moment of the force with respect to point O in the plane of the force $\mathbf{F}$. Point O is called the moment center and the distance d the moment arm.

If the force $\mathbf{F}$ does not lie in a plane perpendicular to the moment axis, it may be resolved into two components, one lying in the plane perpendicular to the moment axis and the other perpendicular to the plane and parallel to the moment axis. *Only the component lying in the plane perpendicular to the moment axis has a moment with respect to that axis*, and the magnitude of its moment is equal to the magnitude of the moment of the force $\mathbf{F}$ with respect to that axis. For example, let the force $\mathbf{F}$ in Fig. 1–10 lie in a plane parallel to the xy plane; the moment

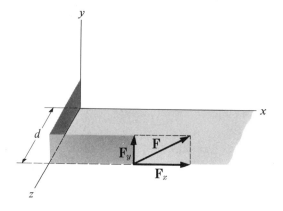

Fig. 1-10

of the force $\mathbf{F}$ with respect to the y axis is desired. The plane perpendicular to the y axis is the xz plane or one parallel thereto. Therefore, resolve the force $\mathbf{F}$ into two components, one $\mathbf{F}_x$ lying in the xz plane and the other $\mathbf{F}_y$ parallel to the y axis. Since $\mathbf{F}_y$ is parallel to the y axis, it has no moment with respect to that axis. Therefore $F_x d$ is the magnitude of the moment of the force $\mathbf{F}$ with respect to the y axis.

In order to find the moment of a force in space with respect to one of the coordinate axes, resolve the force into its three rectangular components parallel to the coordinate axes. The algebraic sum of the moments of the three components with respect to the given axis is equal to the moment of the force with respect to the same axis.

In general, this text deals only with the magnitudes and directions of moments. The method of showing directions of moments is indicated below. The corresponding standard vector notations are listed also.

Direction of Moment	Standard Notation	Text Equivalent
Clockwise looking to right or counterclockwise to left		
Clockwise looking to left or counterclockwise to right		
Clockwise looking upward or counterclockwise downward		
Clockwise looking downward or counterclockwise upward		
Clockwise looking to the rear or counterclockwise forward		
Clockwise looking forward or counterclockwise to rear		

The first symbol indicates the direction a right-hand screw would advance if turned in the direction of the moment, and the second symbol indicates the turning tendency of the moment.

Example 1-5 Determine the moment of the 70-lb force in Fig. 1–11 with respect to the x axis.

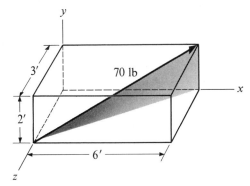

Fig. 1-11

Solution: The length of the 70-lb force s

$$(6^2 + 2^2 + 3^2)^{1/2} = 7 \text{ ft}$$

The x component of the 70-lb force is $70(6/7) = 60$ lb $\rightarrow$

The y component of the 70-lb force is $70(2/7) = 20$ lb $\uparrow$

The z component of the 70-lb force is $70(3/7) = 30$ lb $\nearrow$

The x component is parallel to the x axis and thus has no moment with respect to that axis. The z component passes through the x axis, and thus its moment arm with respect to the x axis is zero. Therefore it also has no moment with respect to the x axis. The y component is perpendicular to a plane in which the x axis lies, and it therefore has a moment with respect to that axis. The moment of the 70-lb force, equivalent to the moment of the y component, with respect to the x axis is $M_x = F_y d = Fd = 20(3)$

$= 60$ ft-lb $\measuredangle$.

Example 1-6a   Determine the moment of the 220-lb force F in Fig. 1–12a with respect to the horizontal line ab.

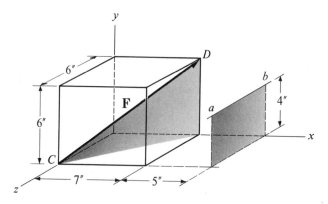

Fig. 1-12a

Solution: The length of the diagonal CD is

$$(7^2 + 6^2 + 6^2)^{1/2} = 11 \text{ in.}$$

The scale for the 220-lb force F is $220/11 = 20$ lb per in. The z-component of F is parallel to ab and thus has no moment with respect to line ab. The x and y components through C are

$$F_x = 20(7) = 140 \text{ lb} \rightarrow$$

$$F_y = 20(6) = 120 \text{ lb} \uparrow$$

The moments of these two forces with respect to the line *ab* are

$$\mathbf{M}_{ab} = 140(4) + 120(12)$$

$$= -560 + 1440 = 880 \text{ in-lb}$$

Example 1-6b   Determine the moments of the forces shown in Fig. 1-12b with respect to point O, which lies in the plane of the forces.

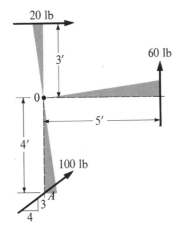

Fig. 1-12b

Solution: Since the magnitude of the moment of a force with respect to a point in the plane of the force is the product of the magnitude of the force and the perpendicular distance between the force and the moment center,

$$\mathbf{M}_O \text{ of the 20-lb force} = 20(3) = 60 \text{ ft-lb}$$

$$\mathbf{M}_O \text{ of the 60-lb force} = 60(5) = 300 \text{ ft-lb}$$

To obtain the moment of the 100-lb force, resolve it into its horizontal and vertical components at point A. The magnitude of the vertical component is

$$\frac{3}{5}(100) = 60 \text{ lb}$$

This component acts through point O and therefore has no moment with respect to point O. The magnitude of the horizontal component is

$$\frac{4}{5}(100) = 80 \text{ lb}$$

The moment of the 100-lb force with respect to point O is equal to the sum of the moments of its 80-lb and 60-lb components with respect to that point:

$$\mathbf{M}_O \text{ of the 100-lb force} = 80(4) + 60(0) = 320 \text{ ft-lb}$$

PROBLEMS

1-18. Determine the moment of the force with respect to the given point A for each of the systems shown in Fig. P 1–18.

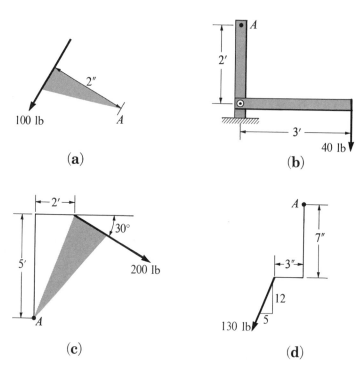

Fig. P 1-18

1-19. Determine the moment of the force with respect to the given point O for each of the systems in Fig. P 1–19.

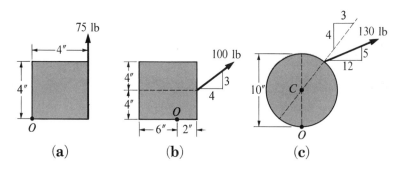

Fig. P 1-19

1-20. A pulley is keyed to the horizontal shaft A in Fig. P 1–20. The tensions in the belt are as shown. Determine the twisting moment transmitted to the shaft by the belt pulley.

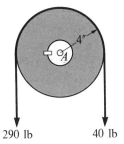

Fig. P 1-20   290 lb   40 lb

1-21. Determine the moment of the force **F** in Fig. P 1–13 with respect to the a axis when the magnitude of F equals 270 lb.

1-22. Determine, with respect to the y axis, the moment of the 70-lb force in Fig. P 1–14.

1-23. Determine, with respect to the a axis, the algehraic sum of the moments of the two forces in Fig. P 1–23.

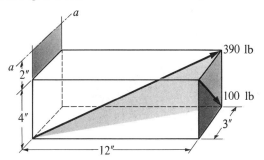

Fig. P 1-23

1-24. The lid of the box shown in Fig. P 1–24 is supported by the strut AB, which exerts a compressive downward force of 20 lb in the direction of the strut. **(a)** Determine the x, y, and z components of this force along the edges of the box at B. **(b)** Determine the moment of the 20-lb force with respect to the edge ab.

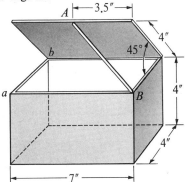

Fig. P 1-24

1-10 PRINCIPLE OF MOMENTS OF FORCES

The principle of moments as applied to a system of forces may be stated as follows: The magnitude of the moment of the resultant of the system of forces with respect to any axis or point is equal to the magnitude of the algebraic sum of the moments of the forces of the system with respect to the axis or point. This principle is applied to areas and volumes in the determination of centroids, centers of gravity, and centers of mass.

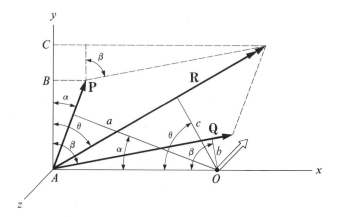

Fig. 1-13

Proof of this principle as applied to forces is as follows: In Fig. 1–13, let **P** and **Q** represent two forces which are concurrent at point *A*. The resultant, according to the parallelogram law, is the diagonal force **R**. A set of rectangular coordinate axes are chosen which have their origin at *A*, the point of intersection of **P** and **Q** on the resultant **R**. Let *O* be any moment center in the plane of the forces located on the *x* axis. Applying the principle of moments, as previously stated,

$$Rc = Pa + Qb$$

where *a*, *b*, and *c* are the moment arms of **P**, **Q**, and **R**, respectively. Let α, β, and θ denote the angles which the action lines of **P**, **Q**, and **R**, respectively, make with the *y* axis. From the figure,

$$AC = AB + BC$$

and therefore

$$R \cos \theta = P \cos \alpha + Q \cos \beta$$

When both sides of this equation are multiplied by *AO*, the following equation is obtained:

$$R(AO) \cos \theta = P(AO) \cos \alpha + Q(AO) \cos \beta$$

Now, since $AO \cos \theta = c$, $AO \cos \alpha = a$, and $AO \cos \beta = b$, therefore $Rc = Pa + Qb$.

The principle of moments is not restricted to only two concurrent forces but may be applied to any force system.

Example 1-7   By the principle of moments, determine the perpendicular distance from the 120-lb force in Fig. 1–14 to point O.

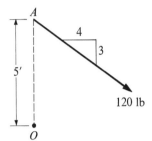

Fig. 1-14

Solution: Since the location of one point (point of application A) on the 120-lb force with respect to point O is known, the force will be resolved into its rectangular components at this point. For convenience, the vertical component is drawn through point O. The components are

$$\mathbf{F}_x = 120\,\frac{4}{5} = 96\,\text{lb} \rightarrow$$

$$\mathbf{F}_y = 120\,\frac{3}{5} = 72\,\text{lb} \downarrow$$

Since the 72-lb force passes through point O, it has no moment with respect to that point. The moment of the 96-lb force is $96(5) = 480$ ft-lb $\curvearrowright$. Since the moments of the components of a force with respect to a moment center are equal to the moment of the force, the 480 ft-lb moment represents the moment of the 120-lb force with respect to point O. Applying the principle of moments,

$$120(a) = 480$$

$$a = \frac{480}{120} = 4\,\text{ft}$$

the perpendicular distance from the 120-lb force to point O.

PROBLEMS

1-25.   The magnitude of the horizontal component of the force **F** shown in Fig. P 1–25 is 80 lb. Determine (a) the force **F**, and (b) the moment of the force **F** with respect to point A. (c) By means of the principle of moments, determine the perpendicular distance from the action line of the force **F** to point *A*.

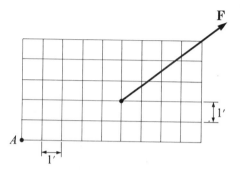

Fig. P 1-25

1-26. (a) Determine the moment of the 100-lb force in Fig. P 1–26 with respect to point *A*. (b) By means of the principle of moments, determine the perpendicular distance from the force to point *A*.

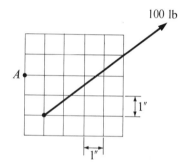

Fig. P 1-26

1-27. (a) Determine the algebraic sum of the moments of the two forces in Fig. P 1–27 with respect to the line *ab*. (b) Use the principle of moments to determine the perpendicular distance from the action line of the 170-lb force to point *A*.

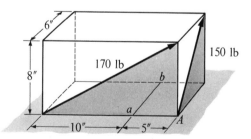

Fig. P 1-27

1-28. Determine the $x, y,$ and z components of the 280-lb force shown in Fig. P 1–28. Also determine the moment of this same force with respect to the line *ab*.

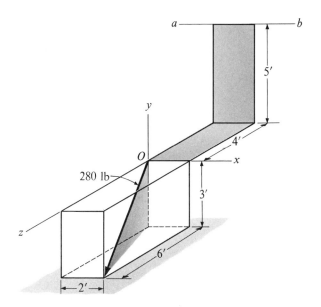

Fig. P 1-28

1-11   COUPLES

A couple consists of two forces which are equal in magnitude and opposite in sense and which have parallel, noncollinear lines of action. A couple has a tendency to rotate a body, but since the sum of the forces of a couple is zero, a couple has no tendency to translate a body. The perpendicular distance between the action lines of the forces of a couple is called the *moment arm. The magnitude of the moment of a couple is equal to the product of the magnitude of one of the forces composing the couple and*

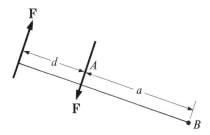

Fig. 1-15

the moment arm of the couple, and the moment vector is perpendicular to the plane of the couple.

The properties which distinguish one couple from another are called its characteristics. *Those characteristics*, which indicate its external effect on a body, *are* (1) *the magnitude of the moment of the couple*, (2) *the slope of the plane of the couple, and* (3) *the direction of rotation of the couple.*

The moment of a couple is constant and independent of the moment center. For example, referring to Fig. 1–15,

$$\mathbf{M}_A = Fd$$

$$\mathbf{M}_B = F(d + a) - Fa = Fd + Fa - Fa = Fd$$

Since the only effect of a couple is to produce a constant moment, *the external effect of a couple on a body is unchanged if* (1) *the couple is rotated through an angle in its plane*, (2) *the couple is translated to another position in its plane*, (3) *the couple is shifted to a parallel plane, and* (4) *the*

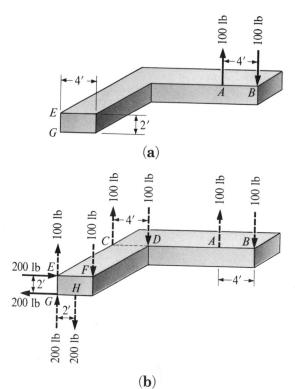

(a)

(b)   **Fig. 1-16**

magnitude of and distance between the forces of the couple are changed providing the magnitude of the couple remains unchanged. These alterations or changes are called transformations of a couple.

Example 1-8 By means of the transformations of a couple, replace the 400 ft-lb couple acting on the frame at A and B in Fig. 1-16a with a couple of the same magnitude and same external effect on the frame whose forces act horizontally at E and G.

Solution: On Fig. 1-16b, translate the couple to points C and D, keeping the distance between the forces and the magnitude of the forces the same. Move the couple from C and D to E and F in a parallel plane. Now move the forces together so that they act at G and H, increasing the magnitude of the forces but keeping the magnitude of the couple the same. Then rotate the couple clockwise 90° so that forces act horizontally at E and G.

The magnitude of the couple is still 400 ft-lb and the external effect on the body has not been changed. Note, however, that the internal effect on the body is different.

1-12 RESOLUTION OF A FORCE INTO A FORCE AND A COUPLE

In some problems of mechanics it is necessary to resolve a force into a force of the same magnitude and sense but with a new line of action and a couple without changing the external effect on the body. For example, in Fig. 1-17, let **P** represent a force acting on the body at point A. Let two equal, opposite, and collinear forces, **P'** and **P''**, be placed at O, each being parallel and equal in magnitude to the original force **P**. The three forces are equivalent to the original force, since the two equal, opposite, and collinear forces have no external effect on the body. The force system is now composed of the force **P'** acting at O, which has the same magnitude and sense as the force **P** at A, and a couple, the moment of which is the same as the moment of the original force **P** with respect

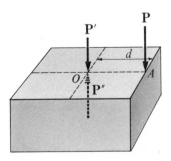

Fig. 1-17

to point O. This couple may be changed in accordance with the transformations of a couple. Thus the original force **P** at point A has been replaced with a force **P′** at point O and a couple whose magnitude is $P(d)$. The force **P′** at point O and the couple whose magnitude is $P(d)$ have the same external effect on the body as the original force **P** at point A.

Example 1-9   Replace the 1000-lb force in Fig. 1-18a by a couple and a force which acts horizontally at the centroid of the cross-section of the beam.

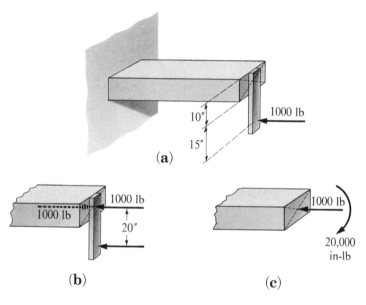

Fig. 1-18

Solution: Place two equal, opposite, and collinear 1000-lb forces at the centroid of the cross-section of the beam as shown in Fig. 1-18b. Since the resultant of these two forces is zero and their moments with respect to any axis are zero, the effect on the beam has not been changed. One of these forces and the original 1000-lb force constitute a couple. The other force at the centroid has the same sense and magnitude as the original force. The magnitude and direction of the couple are

$$\mathbf{C} = 20(1000) = 20{,}000 \text{ in-lb}$$

The force and couple may be indicated as shown in Fig. 1–18c.

Thus the original 1000-lb force at a point 20 in. below the centroid of the cross-section of the beam has been replaced by a force at the centroid of the cross-section and a couple which have the same external effect on the beam as the original force.

PROBLEMS

1-29. Transform the couple shown in Fig. P 1–29 into an equivalent couple whose forces are horizontal and act through points *A* and *B*. Show the couple on a sketch.

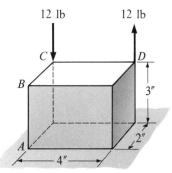

Fig. P 1-29

1-30. Replace the 150 ft-lb counterclockwise couple in Fig. P 1–30 with **(a)** two horizontal forces acting through points *A* and *B*, and **(b)** two vertical forces acting through points *A* and *B*.

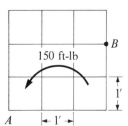

Fig. P 1-30

1-31. The three-step pulley shown in Fig. P 1–31 is subjected to the couples shown. Determine the magnitude of each force of a couple acting at the rim of the 5-in. pulley that is required to balance the system.

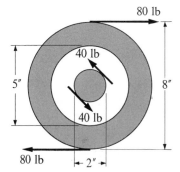

Fig. P 1-31

1-32. Replace the single 60-lb force which drives the ratchet and gear in Fig. P 1–32 by a force which acts at *B* and a couple, the forces of which act horizontally at *A* and *C*.

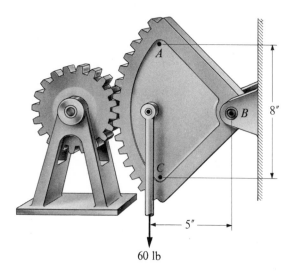

Fig. P 1-32

1-33. Replace the single force in Fig. P 1–33 by a force which acts through *O* and two couples, one parallel to face *CDGH* and the other parallel to face *BDFH*.

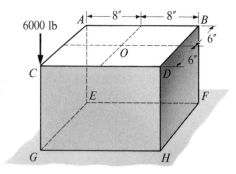

Fig. P 1-33

1-34. Determine the moment of the couple in Fig. P 1–34 with respect to **(a)** point *A*, **(b)** point *B*, and **(c)** point *C*.

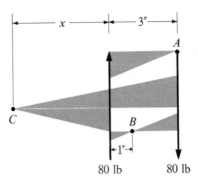

Fig. P 1-34   80 lb   80 lb

1-35. Transform the couple shown in Fig. P 1–35 into an equivalent couple having horizontal forces acting through E and F.

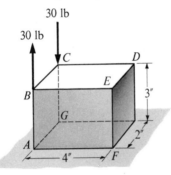

Fig. P 1-35

1-36. Resolve the force and couple shown in Fig. P 1–36 into a force acting through A and a couple whose forces act horizontally through B and C.

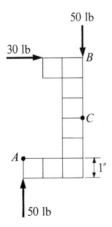

Fig. P 1-36   50 lb

1-37. By means of the transformations of a couple, replace the 50-lb force shown in Fig. P 1–37 by a force and couple, the force acting at *A* and the forces of the couple acting at *B* and *C*. Show each step and do not change the external effect on the body during any operation.

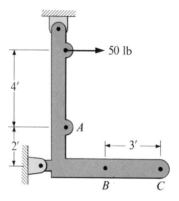

Fig. P 1-37

1-38. Replace the force system shown in Fig. P 1–38 by a single force. Solve by using the method of transformations of a couple. Show each step on a sketch and do not change the external effect in any step.

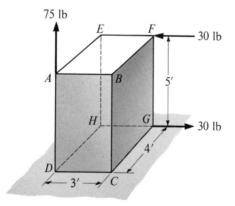

Fig. P 1-38

1-39. By means of the transformations of a couple, replace the 100-lb force acting on the cantilever beam in Fig. P 1–39 by a force at *A* and a a couple whose forces act vertically at *B* and *C*. Do this without changing the external effect on the body and show each step.

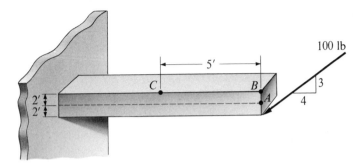

Fig. P 1-39

1-40. Replace the force system shown in Fig. P 1–40 by a single force. Solve by using the method of transformations of a couple. Show each step on a sketch and do not change the external effect in any step.

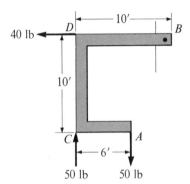

Fig. P 1-40

1-41. Replace the single force acting on the steel gusset plate in Fig. P 1–41 by a horizontal force and a vertical force, both of which act at *B*, and a

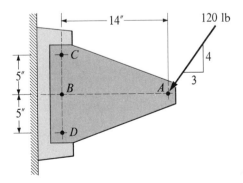

Fig. P 1-41

couple whose forces act horizontally at C and D. Do this without changing the external effect on the body.

1-42. By means of the transformations of a couple, replace the 1000-lb force acting on the steel gusset plate at A in Fig. P 1–42 by a force at C and a couple without changing the external effect on the body. Show each step.

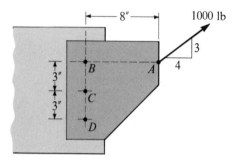

Fig. P 1-42

1-43. A 50-lb force, applied to the wrench as shown in Fig. P 1–43, produces a torque on the square nut on the bolt. Determine the forces between the wrench and the nut at corners A, B, and C if all contact surfaces are assumed to be smooth.

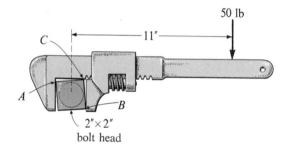

Fig. P 1-43

1-13 DIMENSIONAL EQUATIONS

Algebraic equations represent physical quantities in terms of variables. In most equations relating to engineering, these quantities can be expressed dimensionally in terms of three fundamental quantities: force (F), length (L), and time (T). The following table shows some of the quantities in general engineering use.

All terms of an equation must be of the same dimensions, that is, the equation must be dimensionally homogeneous. For example, consider the equation

$$s = \frac{P}{A} + \frac{Mc}{I}$$

where s is a stress in pounds per square inch (F/L^2), P is a force (F), A is an area (L^2), M is a moment (FL), c is a length (L), and I is inches to the fourth power (L^4). The dimensional equation is

$$\frac{F}{L^2} = \frac{F}{L^2} + FL\left(\frac{L}{L^4}\right) = \frac{F}{L^2} + \frac{F}{L^2}$$

Each term in its final form is in the same dimension: F/L^2; therefore the equation is dimensionally correct.

Table 1

Physical Quantity	Dimensions	Common Engineering Units
Area	L^2	ft², in²
Moment of a force	FL	ft-lb, in-lb
Linear acceleration	L/T^2	fps²
Linear velocity	L/T	fps, mph
Angular velocity	$1/T$	rad per sec, rpm
Volume	L^3	ft³, in³
Mass	FT^2/L	lb-sec² per ft
Sin θ	$L/L = 1$	
Angle	$L/L = 1$	rad, rev, deg
Work	FL	ft-lb, in-lb
Power	FL/T	ft-lb per sec, hp
Linear impulse	FT	lb-sec

Now consider the equation $c^3 + ac^2 = q$, in which c is a length, a is an area, and q is a volume. Since an area is the square of a length (L^2) and a volume is the cube of a length (L^3), the dimensional equation is

$$L^3 + L^4 = L^3$$

Each term in its final form is not in the same dimension (e.g., all are not in L^3), and therefore the equation is dimensionally incorrect.

The use of dimensional equations is helpful in checking any algebraic equations for correctness or in determining the specific units in which a result is to be expressed when computed from a given algebraic equation.

PROBLEMS

Note: In Problems 1-44 through 1-51 all numerical factors are dimensionless unless otherwise specified.

1-44. The equation $S = P/A + Tc/J$ is dimensionally correct. If S is a force per unit area, A is an area, c is a length, and T is the moment of a force, what are the fundamental dimensions of P and J?

1-45. The equation $P/A = S - KL^2/r^2$ is dimensionally correct. If P is a force, A is an area, and L and r are lengths, determine the fundamental dimensions of K and S.

1-46. Determine the fundamental dimensions of V in the expression $V = [2g(h^2 - x^2)^{1/2}]^{1/2}$ if g is the acceleration of gravity, h is a length, and x is a length.

1-47. The equation $Q = K(D - 0.2H)H^{3/2}$ is dimensionally correct. Q is the volume per unit of time, and H is a length. Determine the fundamental dimensions of K and D.

1-48. Is the equation $p/w + v^2/2g = h$ dimensionally correct if p is a force per unit area, v is linear velocity, h represents height, w represents weight per unit volume, and g is the acceleration of gravity?

1-49. Is the equation $Pt = Mv + Wr^2w/2g$ dimensionally correct if P is force, t is time, M is mass, v is linear velocity, W is weight, g is linear acceleration, r is distance, and w is angular velocity?

1-50. Determine the fundamental dimensions of the dimensionally correct expression $P(A - x^2)^{1/2}/g$, where P is a force, A is an area, and g is linear acceleration.

1-51. In the dimensionally correct equation $C\theta = Wv^2/2g - Ph \sin \theta$, θ is an angle, W is a weight, g is a linear acceleration, P is a force, and h is a length. Determine the fundamental dimensions of C and v.

1-14 SUMMARY

A clear understanding of the fundamental concepts underlying statics as covered in this chapter is essential to a proper and ready application of these principles to the problems which follow in succeeding chapters. The following questions provide a short review of these principles and concepts.

1. Define (1) mechanics, and (2) statics.
2. Define a force.
3. Give the characteristics of a force.
4. Differentiate between vector and scalar quantities.
5. State the principle of transmissibility.
6. State the parallelogram law.
7. State the triangle law.
8. Define the moment of a force.
9. State the principle of moments.
10. Define a couple.
11. Give the characteristics of a couple.
12. List the transformations of a couple.

2 ─────────

Resultants of Force
Systems

2-1 INTRODUCTION

The effect of a system of forces on a body may be expressed in terms of a resultant. *A resultant is defined as the simplest equivalent force system to which a given force system may be reduced.* The resultant may be a force, a couple, or a force and a couple. When the sum of the forces acting on a body in a single plane is not zero, the resultant is a force in that plane. When the sum of the forces acting on a body in a single plane is zero but the moments of the forces with respect to any moment center in that plane is not zero, the resultant is a couple in the plane of the forces or a parallel plane. If the resultant is zero (no resultant force or couple), the body is in equilibrium.

If the resultant is not zero, the body is in a state of accelerated motion, giving rise to problems in dynamics. It is desirable to study resultants (1) as a background to the study of dynamics, and (2) in order to more clearly understand how the equations of equilibrium for each type of force system are formulated.

2-2 RESULTANT OF COLLINEAR FORCES

This is the simplest type of force system because the action lines of all forces lie along the same straight line. The magnitude of the resultant of two collinear forces is the algebraic sum of the two magnitudes. The sense of the resultant is the same as the sense of the larger force, and the line of action of the resultant is the same as that of the two forces. Since this resultant can be combined in like manner with any other collinear force, it is evident that the magnitude of the resultant of a system of collinear forces is the algebraic sum of the magnitudes of the individual forces, that the line of action of the resultant is the same as that of the forces of the original system, and that the sense of the resultant is determined from the summation of the forces. The resultant is a single force only. The magnitude of the resultant is determined by means of the equation

$$R = \Sigma F$$

where the summation is taken along the line of action of the forces.

2-3   RESULTANT OF A CONCURRENT, COPLANAR FORCE SYSTEM

A.   Graphic Solution

The resultant of a concurrent, coplanar, unbalanced force system is a single force passing through the point of concurrence. In Fig. 2–1 are shown three such forces, F_1, F_2, and F_3, which act on a body at point O.

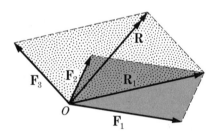

Fig. 2-1

The forces F_1 and F_2 may be combined into a single force R_1 by means of the parallelogram law. In the same way, R_1 and F_3 may be combined into the force R, which then is the resultant of the three original forces F_1, F_2, and F_3. By continuing this process, any number of concurrent forces may be combined into a single resultant force. The order in which the forces are combined is not important. Note that the resultant passes through the point of concurrence. If the resultant of all concurrent forces except the last one is equal to that last force, collinear with it, and of opposite sense, the two forces cancel each other and therefore the resultant is equal to zero and the system of forces is in equilibrium.

Further, the resultant can be obtained by using the triangle law. In Fig. 2–2, start at point O, the point of concurrence, and draw $\mathbf{F}_1$

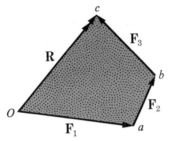

Fig. 2-2

from O to a and then add $\mathbf{F}_2$ from a to b and $\mathbf{F}_3$ from b to c. The resultant is the vector $\mathbf{O}c$, and it is coincident with the resultant vector obtained with the parallelogram law. The polygon constructed as just described is called a *force polygon*, and the forces of the polygon are called *free vectors*. The vector drawn from the tail of the first vector to the tip of the last vector represents completely the resultant of the force system, provided the point of concurrence of all the forces is used as the starting point.

B. Algebraic Solution

In Fig. 2–3b, each of the three forces $\mathbf{F}_1$, $\mathbf{F}_2$, and $\mathbf{F}_3$ of Fig. 2–3a are drawn to form a force polygon and then resolved into rectangular

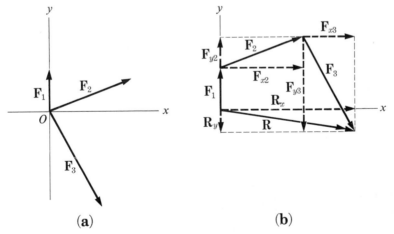

(a)   (b)

Fig. 2-3

components parallel to the x axis and the y axis. The x components of the forces, projected on the x axis, constitute a collinear force system whose resultant is the force $\mathbf{R}_x$ along the x axis. The magnitude of this resultant is equal to the algebraic sum of the x components. The y components of the forces, projected on the y axis, similarly constitute a collinear force system, the resultant of which is the force $\mathbf{R}_y$ along the y axis. $\mathbf{R}_y$ has a magnitude equal to the algebraic sum of the y components. The system of forces is thus reduced to two forces, $\mathbf{R}_x$ and $\mathbf{R}_y$, the magnitude of whose resultant can be determined by the parallelogram law or by the following equation:

$$R = (R_x^2 + R_y^2)^{1/2} = (\Sigma F_x^2 + \Sigma F_y^2)^{1/2}$$

The action line of the resultant must pass through the point of concurrence of the forces. If $\Sigma F_x = 0$ and $\Sigma F_y = 0$, the resultant of the system is zero.

Example 2-1 Determine algebraically the resultant of the concurrent, coplanar force system in Fig. 2-4.

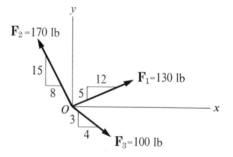

Fig. 2-4

Solution: First reduce each force into its rectangular components in the vertical and horizontal directions.

$$F_{1x} = 130\left(\frac{12}{13}\right) = 120 \text{ lb} \rightarrow$$

$$F_{1y} = 130\left(\frac{5}{13}\right) = 50 \text{ lb} \uparrow$$

$$F_{2x} = 170\left(\frac{8}{17}\right) = 80 \text{ lb} \leftarrow$$

$$F_{2y} = 170\left(\frac{15}{17}\right) = 150 \text{ lb} \uparrow$$

$$F_{3x} = 100\left(\frac{4}{5}\right) = 80 \text{ lb} \rightarrow$$

$$F_{3y} = 100\left(\frac{3}{5}\right) = 60 \text{ lb} \downarrow$$

Tabulating the vertical and horizontal component forces gives

$$\mathbf{R}_x = 120 - 80 + 80 = 120 \text{ lb} \rightarrow$$
$$\mathbf{R}_y = 50 + 150 - 60 = 140 \text{ lb} \uparrow$$

from which

$$\mathbf{R} = (R_x^2 + R_y^2)^{1/2} = (120^2 + 140^2)^{1/2} = 184.5 \text{ lb } 14\!\!\nearrow^{12} \quad \text{through } O$$

The angle that the resultant makes with the x axis may be computed as follows:

$$\theta = \tan^{-1}\!\left(\frac{14}{12}\right) = \tan^{-1}(1.166) = 49°23'$$

Since the slope is more readily determined, it is suggested that the slope be designated instead of the angle.

Example 2-2   The 120-lb force in Fig. 2-5 is the resultant of a coplanar, concurrent force system consisting of the 60-1b force shown and one other force. Determine completely the unknown force.

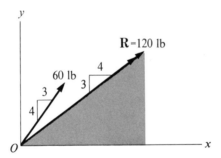

Fig. 2-5

Solution: The x component of the resultant force must equal the sum of the x components of the known and unknown forces. Thus,

$$120\!\left(\frac{4}{5}\right) = 60\!\left(\frac{3}{5}\right) + F_x$$
$$96 = 36 + F_x$$

and

$$F_x = 60 \text{ lb} \rightarrow$$

Also, the y component of the resultant force must equal the sum of the y components of the known and unknown forces. Thus,

$$120\left(\frac{3}{5}\right) = 60\left(\frac{4}{5}\right) + F_y$$

$$72 = 48 + F_y$$

and

$$\mathbf{F}_y = 24 \text{ lb } \uparrow$$

Therefore, $\mathbf{F} = (60^2 + 24^2)^{1/2} = 64.7$ lb through O, the point of concurrence.

PROBLEMS

2-1. A tug-of-war between four men, two on each side, results in the collinear force system shown in Fig. P 2–1. Determine the resultant.

Fig. P 2-1

2-2. (a) To what simplest equivalent system can a concurrent, coplanar force system be reduced? (b) Determine completely the resultant of the coplanar force system in Fig. P 2–2 and show it on a sketch of the system.

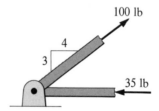

Fig. P 2-2

2-3. Determine completely the resultant of the coplanar force system in Fig. P 2–3 and show it on a sketch of the system.

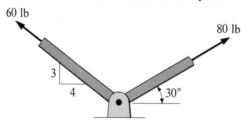

Fig. P 2-3

2-4. Determine completely the resultant of the coplanar force system in Fig. P 2–4 and show it on a sketch of the system.

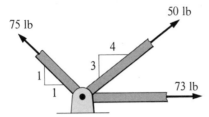

Fig. P 2-4

2-5. Determine completely the resultant of the coplanar force system shown in Fig. P 2–5 and locate it on a sketch of the system.

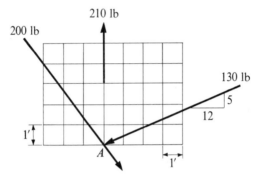

Fig. P 2-5

2-6. Three anchored ships exert the coplanar forces indicated in Fig. P 2–6 on the anchor post on the wharf. Determine the resultant force. All forces are in the *xz* plane.

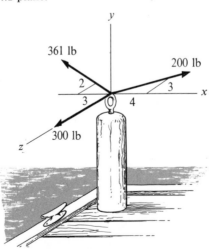

Fig. P 2-6

2-7. Determine the resultant of the coplanar force system in Fig. P 2–7.

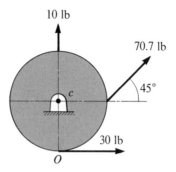

Fig. P 2-7

2-8. The resultant of the three forces shown in Fig. P 2–8 acts horizontally. Determine the magnitude and sense of the resultant.

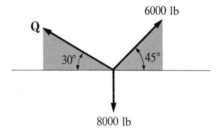

Fig. P 2-8

2-9. The 160-lb force of Fig. P 2–9 is the resultant of a coplanar, concurrent force system consisting of the 30-lb force shown and two other forces not shown. The action line of one of the unknown forces is horizontal, and that of the other has a slope of 3 upward to 4 to the left. Determine completely the two unknown forces.

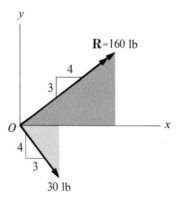

Fig. P 2-9

2-10. Determine the resultant of the three forces acting on the bracket in Fig. P 2–10.

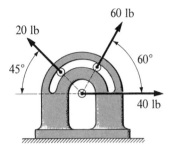

Fig. P 2-10

2-11. Determine completely the resultant of the force system in Fig. P 2–11 and show it on a sketch.

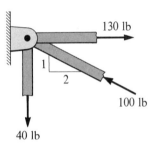

Fig. P 2-11   40 lb

2-12. Determine completely the resultant of the coplanar force system shown in Fig. P 2–12.

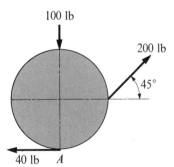

Fig. P 2-12   40 lb   *A*

2-13. Determine completely the resultant of the coplanar force system shown in Fig. P 2–13.

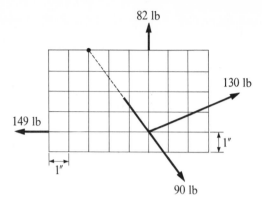

Fig. P 2-13

2-14. The 100-lb force shown in Fig. P 2–14 is the resultant of two forces, one of which is the 50-lb force shown. Determine the other force.

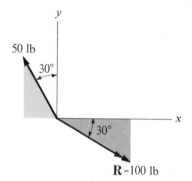

Fig. P 2-14

2-15. The 20-lb force shown in Fig. P 2–15 is the resultant of two forces, one of which is the 78-lb force shown. Determine completely the other force and show it on a sketch.

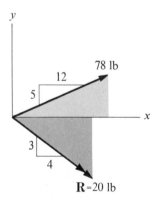

Fig. P 2-15

2-16. Determine completely the resultant of the coplanar forces acting on the gusset plate in Fig. P 2–16.

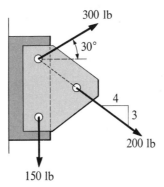

Fig. P 2-16

2-17. Determine completely the resultant of the coplanar forces acting on the cables in the ring in Fig. P 2–17.

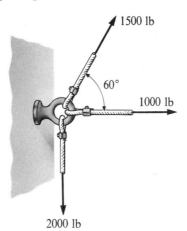

Fig. P 2-17

2-4 BOW'S NOTATION FOR GRAPHIC SOLUTIONS

A method of labeling forces known as "Bow's notation" is used generally with force and space diagrams. A diagram showing the forces in their proper positions is referred to as a *space diagram.* A force diagram or polygon consists of two or more vectors drawn in series to represent the forces in magnitude and direction but not showing their corresponding lines of action. When Bow's notation is used, the spaces on either side

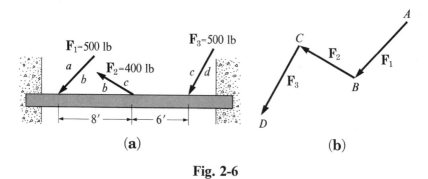

Fig. 2-6

of each external force on the space diagram are labeled with lower-case letters as shown in Fig. 2–6a. On the force polygon each force vector is designated by the corresponding capital letters, as shown in Fig. 2–6b. For example, in Fig. 2–6a, the action line F_1 is labeled ab, while in Fig. 2–6b, the force F_1 is represented by the vector **AB**. The forces in the space diagram should be labeled consistently in either the clockwise or counterclockwise directions.

2-5 RESULTANT OF A NONCONCURRENT, COPLANAR FORCE SYSTEM

A. Graphic Solution

The resultant of a system of nonconcurrent, coplanar forces may be either a force or a couple and can be obtained either by applying the parallelogram law or by means of a force and string polygon. Fig. 2–7 illustrates the use of the parallelogram law.

Forces F_1 and F_2 are moved along their lines of action to their point of intersection by the principle of transmissibility. The resultant R_1 of these two forces is determined by constructing a parallelogram. The resultant R_1 is then combined in the same manner with the force F_3 to obtain the resultant R, which is the resultant of the three forces F_1, F_2, and F_3. The resultant R so determined will be complete since it will have the correct magnitude and sense and will be located on its proper line of action. In case the resultant obtained by combining all forces except the last one of a force system is equal, opposite, and parallel to the last force, the resultant and the last force constitute a couple. In case the resultant so determined is equal, opposite, and collinear to the last force, the two will cancel each other and the resultant of all the forces will be zero.

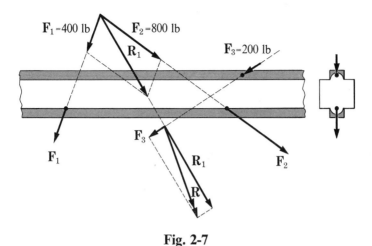

Fig. 2-7

The method of parallelograms may become quite involved when the system is composed of many forces. The force and string polygon method is more convenient and more generally used in such cases. Using the force system acting on the cantilever beam in Fig. 2–8a, one constructs the force polygon shown in Fig. 2–8b. Any point O is selected and rays are

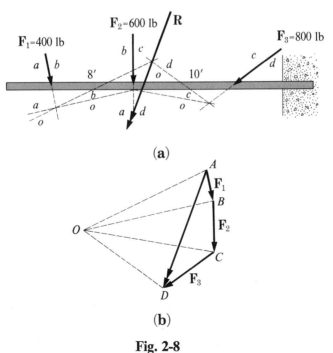

(a)

(b)

Fig. 2-8

drawn to points A, B, C, and D. These rays (strings), together with the forces of the force polygon, constitute a *string polygon*. Force $\mathbf{F}_1$ (**AB** on the diagram) has two nonrectangular components which have magnitudes represented by AO and OB. The action lines of these components are shown on the space diagram in Fig. 2–8a as *ao* and *ob* intersecting at any point on $\mathbf{F}_1$. Next, force $\mathbf{F}_2$ has two components having magnitudes represented by BO and OC and lines of action on the space diagram along *bo* and *oc*. Similarly, the components of **CD**, with magnitudes represented by CO and OD, have lines of action along *co* and *od*. Since the components **OB** of $\mathbf{F}_1$ and **BO** of $\mathbf{F}_2$ have the same magnitude and line of action but opposite sense, they cancel each other. In the same manner all components are canceled except the first and last components, **AO** along *ao* and **OD** along *od*. Therefore the resultant must pass through the point of intersection of *ao* and *od* and have the magnitude and sense indicated by **AD** on the force polygon. If A and D are coincident (**AO** and **OD** are collinear), the resultant force is zero, and if the action lines *ao* and *od* are parallel but not collinear, the resultant is a couple. The magnitude of such a couple would be the magnitude of the vector force **AO** or **OD** multiplied by the perpendicular distance between the action lines *ao* and *od*.

Where all forces of a system are parallel, the resultant may be obtained graphically by use of the force and string polygon in the same way as above. The only change is that the force polygon becomes a straight line.

B. Algebraic Solution

In order to determine the magnitude of the resultant of a nonconcurrent, coplanar force system algebraically, each force is replaced by its rectangular x and y components and the magnitude determined by the following equations:

$$\Sigma F_x = R_x \qquad \Sigma F_y = R_y$$

$$R = (\Sigma F_x^2 + \Sigma F_y^2)^{1/2} \qquad \tan \theta_x = \frac{R_y}{R_x}$$

When the algebraic sums of the forces in the x and y directions are zero, the resultant is not a force but may be a couple in the plane of the forces. If the algebraic sum of the moments of the forces also is zero, the resultant is neither a force nor a couple but it is zero, and the body is in equilibrium.

The location of a point on the action line of the resultant is determined by the principle of moments, which states that the magnitude of the moment of the resultant with respect to an axis perpendicular to the plane of the forces, or with respect to a moment center in the plane of the forces, equals the magnitude of the algebraic sum of the moments of the forces of the system with respect to the same axis or moment center. Thus

$$Rq = \Sigma M_o$$

where q is the perpendicular distance from the moment axis through point O to the resultant force **R**. The direction from O to **R** is determined from the sense of **R** and of the ΣM_o.

In case of a parallel, coplanar force system with the forces parallel to the y axis, the magnitude of the resultant can be determined from the two equations

$$\Sigma F_y = R \quad \text{and} \quad R\bar{x} = \Sigma M_o$$

where $\bar{x}$ is the perpendicular distance from the resultant to the moment axis at O, and ΣM_o is the magnitude of the summation of the moments of the forces of the system with respect to the same axis at O.

Example 2-3 Determine the resultant of the force system in Fig. 2-9a and show it on a sketch located with respect to point A.

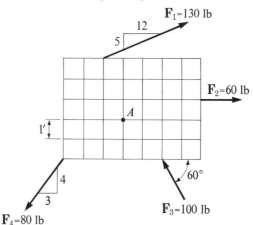

Fig. 2-9a

Solution: First, reduce each force into its vertical and horizontal components as follows:

$$F_{1x} = 130\left(\frac{12}{13}\right) = 120 \text{ lb} \rightarrow$$

$$F_{1y} = 130\left(\frac{5}{13}\right) = 50 \text{ lb} \uparrow$$

$$F_{3x} = 100(0.500) = 50 \text{ lb} \leftarrow$$

$$F_{3y} = 100(0.866) = 86.6 \text{ lb} \uparrow$$

$$F_{4x} = 80\left(\frac{3}{5}\right) = 48 \text{ lb} \leftarrow$$

$$F_{4y} = 80\left(\frac{4}{5}\right) = 64 \text{ lb} \downarrow$$

The horizontal force $\mathbf{F}_2 = 60 \text{ lb} \rightarrow$

Tabulating the vertical and horizontal components,

$$\mathbf{R}_x = 120 + 60 - 50 - 48 = 82 \text{ lb} \rightarrow$$
$$\mathbf{R}_y = 50 + 86.6 - 64 = 72.6 \text{ lb} \uparrow$$

$$\mathbf{R} = (82^2 + 72.6^2)^{1/2} = 109.5 \text{ lb} \quad \underset{82}{\diagup}^{72.6}$$

Next locate the action line of the resultant force with respect to point A. By the principle of moments, the magnitude of the moment of the resultant with respect to point A equals the magnitude of the algebraic sum of the moments of the forces with respect to the same point. Thus,

$$
\begin{array}{llll}
109.5(a) = (120)(3) & (86.6)(2) = & 360 & 173.2 \\
(\ 50)(1) & (64.0)(3) = & 50 & 192.0 \\
(\ 60)(1) & = & 60 & \\
(\ 50)(2) & = & 100 & \\
(\ 48)(2) & = & 96 & \\
& & \overline{666} & \overline{365.2} \\
& & -365.2 & \\
109.5(a) & = & \overline{300.8} &
\end{array}
$$

Thus, $a = 300.8/109.5 = 2.75$ ft, as shown in Fig. 2–9b.

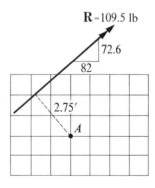

$\mathbf{R} = 109.5 \text{ lb}$

72.6

82

2.75′

A

Fig. 2-9b

The direction and slope of the resultant is determined by the magnitude and direction of each of the resultant components, and the moment is clockwise, as determined from the summation of the moments of the forces of the system.

Example 2-4 The 160-lb force $\mathbf{R}$ of Fig. 2-10a is the resultant of three forces, two of which are shown. Determine the third force, $\mathbf{F}_3$, and locate it with respect to point A.

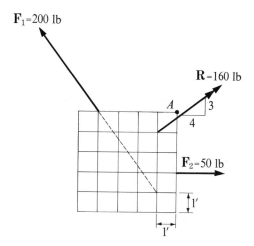

Fig. 2-10a

Solution: The magnitude of the sum of the x components of the unknown and the known forces is equal to the magnitude of the x component of the resultant force. Thus,

$$160\left(\frac{4}{5}\right) = 50 - 200\left(\frac{3}{5}\right) + F_{3x}$$

$$128 = 50 - 120 + F_{3x}$$

and

$$\mathbf{F}_{3x} = 198 \text{ lb} \rightarrow$$

Also, the magnitude of the sum of the y components of the unknown and the known forces is equal to the magnitude of the y component of the resultant force. Thus,

$$160\left(\frac{3}{5}\right) = 200\left(\frac{4}{5}\right) + F_{3y}$$

$$96 = 160 + F_{3y}$$

and

$$\mathbf{F}_{3y} = -64 \text{ lb or } 64 \text{ lb} \downarrow$$

Therefore,

$$\mathbf{F}_3 = (198^2 + 64^2)^{1/2} = 208 \text{ lb} \underset{64}{\overset{198}{\searcular}}$$

Then, by the principle of moments, $Ra = \Sigma M_A$. That is,

$$96(1) + 128(1) = 160(4) + 50(3)$$
$$208(a)$$

$$96 - 128 = 640 + 208a - 150$$

and

$$208a = -522$$

$$a = -2.51 \text{ ft}$$

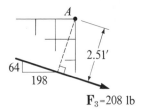

Fig. 2-10b

Since the moment of the unknown force was assumed clockwise and the result is negative, the moment of the force is counterclockwise with respect to point A and therefore is located as shown in Fig. 2–10b.

Example 2-5 Determine the resultant of the coplanar force system acting on the I-beam shown in Fig. 2–11.

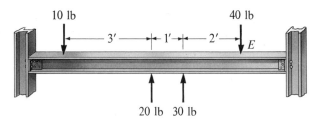

Fig. 2-11

Solution: Since this is a parallel force system, the summation of the forces in the vertical or y direction gives the magnitude and direction of the resultant force.

$$\Sigma \mathbf{F}_y = \mathbf{R} = 20 + 30 - 10 - 40 = 0$$

where the plus direction is taken upward. The resultant force is zero. However, there may be a resultant couple.

$$\Sigma \mathbf{M}_E = 20(3) + 30(2) - 10(6) = 60 \text{ ft-lb} \enspace \curvearrowright$$

The resultant in this case is a couple of 60 ft-lb clockwise, since clockwise moments are positive in the moment equation.

Since neither the magnitude of the forces nor the moment arm of this couple is known, any pair of forces separated by a distance which gives a clockwise moment of 60 ft-lb will constitute the couple. Such a couple can consist of two 30-lb forces 2 ft apart or two 15-lb forces 4 ft apart, etc. In the above example the resultant is completely defined by specifying it to be a clockwise couple with a magnitude of 60 ft-lb.

Example 2-6 The resultant of four forces and an unknown couple acting on the cantilever H-beam in Fig. 2–12 is 20 lb acting vertically downward, 8 ft to the left of point B. Determine the magnitude of the unknown couple.

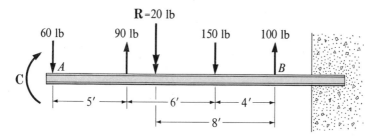

Fig. 2-12

Solution: Since the magnitude of the sum of the moments of all the forces and the couple must be equal to the magnitude of the moment of the resultant force with respect to any point such as point B in the plane of the forces—that is, $R(a) = \Sigma M_B$,—therefore summing moments with respect to point B gives

$$20(8) = C \quad\quad + 150(4)$$
$$90(10) \quad\quad 60(15)$$
$$160 = -900 - C + 600 + 900$$

and

$$C = 440 \text{ ft-lb} \searrow$$

PROBLEMS

2-18. Determine the resultant of the coplanar force system shown in Fig. P 2–18 with respect to point A.

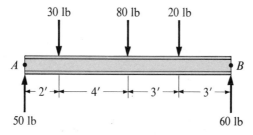

Fig. P 2-18

2-19. Determine the resultant of the coplanar force system shown in Fig. P 2–19 with respect to point *A*.

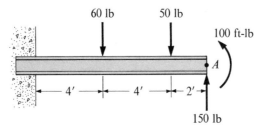

Fig. P 2-19

2-20. Determine completely the resultant of the coplanar force system shown in Fig. P 2–20 and locate it on a sketch of the system with respect to point *A*.

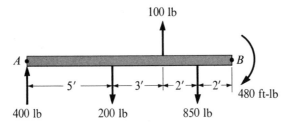

Fig. P 2-20

2-21. The resultant of four parallel forces (one force is not shown) is **R** = 25 lb upward as indicated in Fig. P 2–21. Determine completely the missing force with respect to point *A*.

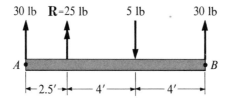

Fig. P 2-21

2-22. The force **R** = 37 lb upward in Fig. P 2–22 is the resultant of three forces, two of which are shown on the figure. Determine the third force.

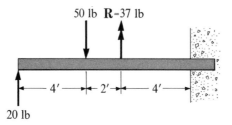

Fig. P 2-22

2-23. Determine completely the resultant of the coplanar force system in Fig. P 2–23 and show it on a sketch of the system with respect to point *A*.

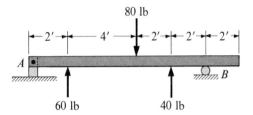

Fig. P 2-23

2-24. Determine completely the resultant of the coplanar force system shown in Fig. P 2–24 and locate it on a dimensioned sketch of the system with respect to point *A*.

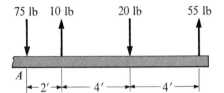

Fig. P 2-24

2-25. Determine completely the resultant of the coplanar force system in Fig. P 2–25 and show it on a dimensioned sketch of the system with respect to point *A*.

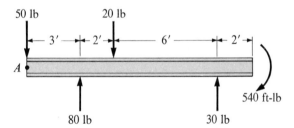

Fig. P 2-25

2-26. Determine completely the resultant of the coplanar force system in Fig. P 2–26 and show it on a sketch of the system.

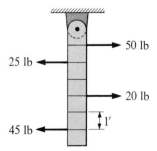

Fig. P 2-26

2-27. A truss is loaded as shown in Fig. P 2–27. Determine the resultant load on the truss with respect to point *A*.

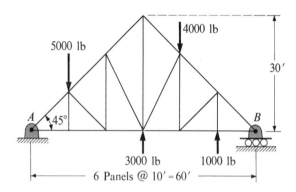

Fig. P 2-27

2-28. Determine completely the resultant of the three forces in Fig. P 2–28 and locate it on a sketch with respect to the center of the wheel.

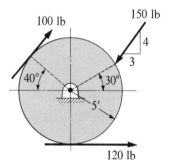

Fig. P 2-28

2-29. Determine completely the resultant of the parallel coplanar force system in Fig. P 2–29 and show it on a sketch with respect to point *C*.

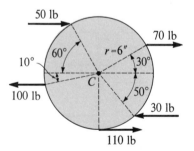

Fig. P 2-29

2-30. Determine the resultant of the coplanar force system shown in Fig. P 2–30 and locate it on a sketch with respect to point A on the wheel.

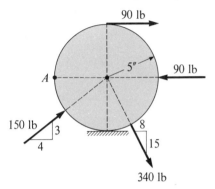

Fig. P 2-30

2-31. The 58.9-lb force shown in Fig. P 2–31 is the resultant of three forces, two of which are shown. Determine completely the other force and show it located on a sketch with respect to point A.

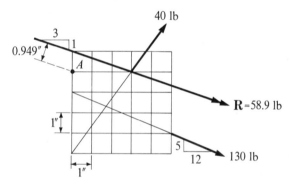

Fig. P 2-31

2-32. For the coplanar force system shown in Fig. P 2–32 determine the resultant completely and locate it on a sketch with respect to point A.

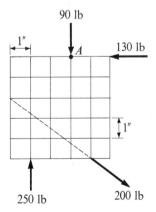

Fig. P 2-32

2-33. Determine completely the resultant of the coplanar force system shown in Fig. P 2–33 and locate it on a sketch with respect to point *A*.

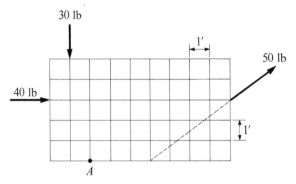

Fig. P 2-33

2-34. Determine the resultant of the coplanar force system shown in Fig. P 2–34 and locate it on a sketch with respect to point *O*.

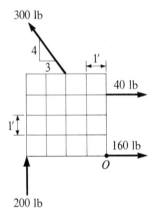

Fig. P 2-34

2-35. Given the coplanar force system shown in Fig. P 2–35, determine the resultant completely.

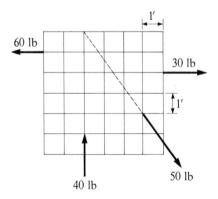

Fig. P 2-35

2-36. Given the coplanar force system shown in Fig. P 2–36, determine the resultant completely and locate it on a sketch with respect to point *A*.

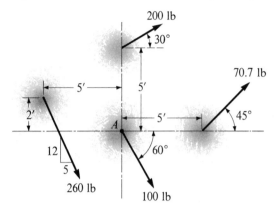

Fig. P 2-36

2-37. Determine completely the resultant of the coplanar force system in Fig. P 2–37 and show it on a sketch of the system with respect to the origin.

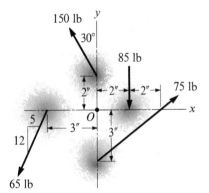

Fig. P 2-37

2-38. Determine the resultant of the parallel force system shown in Fig. P 2–38 by means of a graphical solution.

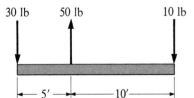

Fig. P 2-38

2-39. Determine graphically the resultant of the coplanar force system shown in Fig. P 2–18.

2-40. Determine graphically the resultant of the coplanar force system shown in Fig. P 2–27.

2-41. Determine graphically the resultant of the coplanar force system shown in Fig. P 2–23.

2-42. Determine graphically the resultant of the coplanar force system shown in Fig. P 2–24.

2-43. Determine graphically the resultant of the coplanar force system shown in Fig. P 2–26.

2-6   RESULTANT OF A CONCURRENT, NONCOPLANAR FORCE SYSTEM

A.   Graphic Method

The resultant of a system of noncoplanar, concurrent forces is a force acting through the point of concurrence of the forces. The resultant may be determined by constructing a force polygon starting at the point of concurrence. The line drawn from the beginning of the first vector to the end of the last vector of the polygon is the vector which represents the resultant of the system of forces in magnitude and direction. The force polygon is not a plane polygon, however, and therefore the graphic method of determining the resultant of this system or any other non-coplanar force system is not as easily used as the algebraic method. For this reason the algebraic method only will be discussed for non-coplanar force systems.

B.   Algebraic Method

Any noncoplanar force may be resolved into three mutually perpendicular components parallel to their coordinate axes as explained in Sec. 1–8. When a number of forces intersect at a common point, that point may be taken as the origin of the axes and all forces of the system resolved into components along these three axes. Then the magnitudes of the components along these axes can be added algebraically to give the magnitudes of the three components of the resultant, thus:

$$\Sigma F_x = R_x \qquad \Sigma F_y = R_y \qquad \Sigma F_z = R_z$$

The magnitude of the resultant of the forces of the system, therefore, is the vector sum of the resulting components, that is

$$R = (R_x^2 + R_y^2 + R_z^2)^{1/2}$$

and

$$\cos \theta_x = \frac{R_x}{R} \qquad \cos \theta_y = \frac{R_y}{R} \qquad \cos \theta_z = \frac{R_z}{R}$$

where θ_x, θ_y, and θ_z are the angles which the action line of the resultant makes with the coordinate axes as shown in Fig. 2–13.

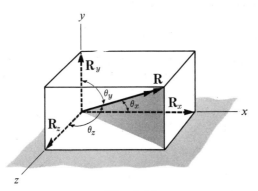

Fig. 2-13

Example 2-7   Given the following noncoplanar force system which is concurrent at the origin and which has all forces directed from the origin toward the points indicated, determine the resultant completely:

Magnitude of Force	x, y, z Coordinates of Point
$F_1 = 70$ lb	2, −6, 3
$F_2 = 120$ lb	−2, 1, −2
$F_3 = 90$ lb	1, 2, 2

Solution: First resolve the forces into their x, y, and z components. The length of each force vector is

$$L_{70} = (2^2 + 6^2 + 3^2)^{1/2} = 7$$
$$L_{120} = (2^2 + 1^2 + 2^2)^{1/2} = 3$$
$$L_{90} = (1^2 + 2^2 + 2^2)^{1/2} = 3$$

Resolving the forces into their components,

$$F_{1x} = 70\left(\frac{2}{7}\right) = 20 \text{ lb}$$
$$F_{2x} = 120\left(\frac{-2}{3}\right) = -80 \text{ lb} \qquad R_x = 20 - 80 + 30 = -30 \text{ lb}$$
$$F_{3x} = 90\left(\frac{1}{3}\right) = 30 \text{ lb}$$

$$F_{1y} = 70\left(\frac{-6}{7}\right) = -60 \text{ lb}$$
$$F_{2y} = 120\left(\frac{1}{3}\right) = 40 \text{ lb} \qquad R_y = 40 + 60 - 60 = 40 \text{ lb}$$
$$F_{3y} = 90\left(\frac{2}{3}\right) = 60 \text{ lb}$$

$$F_{1z} = 70\left(\frac{3}{7}\right) = 30 \text{ lb}$$

$$F_{2z} = 120\left(\frac{-2}{3}\right) = -80 \text{ lb} \qquad R_z = 30 - 80 + 60 = 10 \text{ lb}$$

$$F_{3z} = 90\left(\frac{2}{3}\right) = 60 \text{ lb}$$

Therefore, $R = (30^2 + 40^2 + 10^2)^{1/2} = 51$ lb passing from origin through a point having x, y, z coordinates of $-3, 4, 1$ respectively.

Example 2-8 Given the following noncoplanar force system, which is concurrent at the origin and which has all forces directed from the origin toward the points indicated, determine the resultant.

Magnitude of Force	x, y, z Coordinates of Point
$F_1 = 80$ lb	$3, \; -4, \quad 2$
$F_2 = 60$ lb	$-2, \quad 3, \; -5$
$F_3 = 90$ lb	$1, \quad 2, \quad 2$

Solution: First resolve the forces into their x, y, and z components. The length of each force vector is

$$L_{80} = (3^2 + 4^2 + 2^2)^{1/2} = 5.39$$
$$L_{60} = (2^2 + 3^2 + 5^2)^{1/2} = 6.17$$
$$L_{90} = (1^2 + 2^2 + 2^2)^{1/2} = 3.00$$

Resolving the forces into their components,

$$F_{1x} = 80\left(\frac{3}{5.39}\right) = 44.5 \text{ lb}$$

$$F_{2x} = 60\left(\frac{-2}{6.17}\right) = -19.5 \text{ lb} \qquad R_x = 44.5 - 19.5 + 30 = 55.0 \text{ lb}$$

$$F_{3x} = 90\left(\frac{1}{3}\right) = 30.0 \text{ lb}$$

$$F_{1y} = 80\left(\frac{-4}{5.39}\right) = -59.3 \text{ lb}$$

$$F_{2y} = 60\left(\frac{3}{6.17}\right) = 29.2 \text{ lb} \qquad R_y = -59.3 + 29.2 + 60 = 29.9 \text{ lb}$$

$$F_{3y} = 90\left(\frac{2}{3}\right) = 60.0 \text{ lb}$$

$$F_{1z} = 80\left(\frac{2}{5.39}\right) = 29.7 \text{ lb}$$

$$F_{2z} = 60\left(\frac{-5}{6.17}\right) = -48.7 \text{ lb} \qquad R_z = 29.7 - 48.7 + 60 = 41.0 \text{ lb}$$

$$F_{3z} = 90\left(\frac{2}{3}\right) = 60.0 \text{ lb}$$

Therefore, $R = (55.0^2 + 29.9^2 + 41.0^2)^{1/2} = 74.8$ lb passing from origin through a point having the x, y, z coordinates of 55.0, 29.9, 41.0 respectively.

PROBLEMS

2-44. Given the three concurrent forces shown in Fig. P 2–44, determine the moment of the resultant of this system with respect to the x axis.

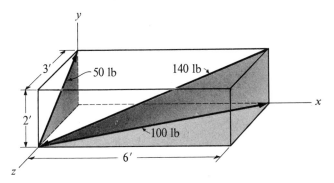

Fig. P 2-44

2-45. Determine the resultant of the two forces shown in Fig. P 2–45 and show it on a sketch. Also determine the moment of the resultant about the z axis.

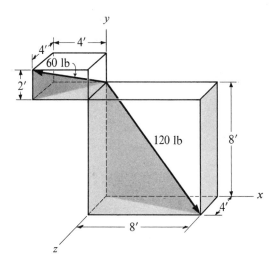

Fig. P 2-45

2-46. Determine the resultant of the 30-lb force and the 10-lb force in Fig. P 2–46 and locate it on a sketch.

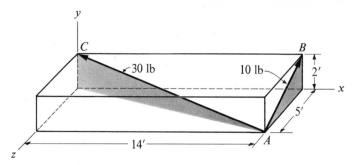

Fig. P 2-46

2-47.   In Fig. P 2–47 determine: **(a)** the x, y, and z components of the 39-lb force; **(b)** the moment of the 39-lb force with respect to the ab axis; **(c)** the resultant of the 10-lb and 39-lb forces.

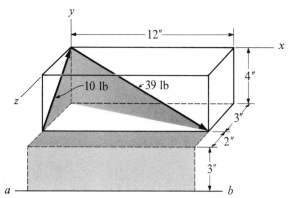

Fig. P 2-47

2-48.   **(a)** Determine the resultant of the forces shown in Fig. P 2–48. **(b)** Determine the moment of the resultant of the forces shown in Fig. P 2–48 with respect to the line ab.

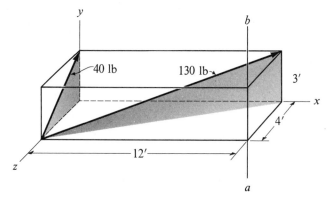

Fig. P 2-48

2-49. Determine the resultant of the forces shown in Fig. P 2–49 and locate it on a sketch.

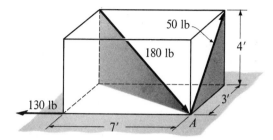

Fig. P 2-49

2-50. Determine the resultant of the three concurrent forces shown in Fig. P 2–50.

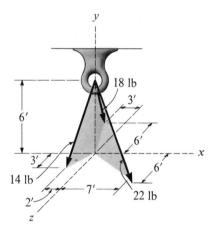

Fig. P 2-50

In each of the Problems 2–51 through 2–54 the action line of the given force passes from the origin through the indicated point. The positive directions of the coordinate axes are as shown in Fig. P 2–51. In each problem determine completely the resultant of the forces.

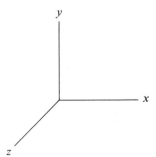

Fig. P 2-51

2-51. Force: 210 lb   130 lb
        x, y, z: 2, -6, -3 0, 5, -12

2-52. Force: 70 lb   60 lb   90 lb
        x, y, z: 2, 6, -3 1, -2, 2 -2, 1, 2

2-53. Force: 90 lb   140 lb   60 lb
        x, y, z: 1, -2, 2   2, 6, -3 2, -1, -2

2-54. Force: 100 lb   75 lb   90 lb
        x, y, z: 3, 4, 6 $-2, 5, -7$ 2, 1, 2

2-7 RESULTANT OF A NONCOPLANAR, PARALLEL FORCE SYSTEM

Algebraic Method

The resultant of a noncoplanar, parallel system of forces is either a single force or a couple in a plane parallel to the forces. In order to determine the resultant of such a system, select the coordinate axes so that one axis is parallel to the forces. Fig. 2–14 shows a system of parallel forces parallel to the y axis. If the resultant is a single force, its magnitude and sense are determined by the algebraic sum of the forces of the system.

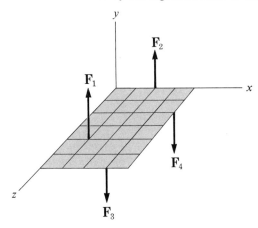

Fig. 2-14

The line of action of the resultant is found by applying the principle of moments. Thus, if the magnitude of the algebraic sum of the moments of the forces with respect to the x axis is indicated by ΣM_x, and the distance of the resultant from the x axis by $\bar{z}$, then by the principle of moments, $R\bar{z} = \Sigma M_x$. In the same way $R\bar{x} = \Sigma M_z$. The resultant therefore is completely determined by the equations

$$\mathbf{R} = \Sigma \mathbf{F}_y \qquad R\bar{z} = \Sigma M_x \qquad R\bar{x} = \Sigma M_z$$

If the ΣF_y equals zero, the resultant is not a force but may be a couple. If the summation of moments of the forces with respect to the x or z axis is not zero, the resultant is a couple. The moment $\mathbf{C}_x$ of the resultant couple with respect to the x axis is equal to the algebraic sum of the moments of the forces of the system with respect to the x axis. That is, $\mathbf{C}_x = \Sigma \mathbf{M}_x$. Similarly, $\mathbf{C}_z = \Sigma \mathbf{M}_z$. $\mathbf{C}_x$ and $\mathbf{C}_z$ lie in or are parallel to the yz and xy planes, respectively, and are components of the resultant couple. The magnitude of the resultant couple is given by the equation

$$C = (\Sigma M_x^2 + \Sigma M_z^2)^{1/2} = (C_x^2 + C_z^2)^{1/2}$$

Example 2-9   Determine the resultant of the four parallel forces in Fig. 2–15a and show it on a sketch.

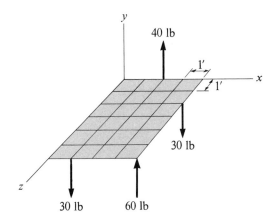

Fig. 2-15a

Solution: The forces of the system can be tabulated thus:

↑	↓
40	30
60	30
100	60

$$-60$$
$$\mathbf{R} = \quad 40 \text{ lb } \uparrow$$

The magnitude of the moments of the forces with respect to the x axis are as follows:

$$\Sigma M_x = R\bar{z} = 40(\bar{z}) = (6)(60) \qquad (30)(2) = \quad 360 \qquad 60$$
$$(30)(6) \qquad \qquad 180$$
$$\overline{\quad\quad\quad} \qquad \overline{\quad\quad\quad}$$
$$360 \qquad 240$$
$$-240$$
$$\overline{\quad\quad\quad\quad}$$
$$120 \text{ ft-lb}$$

$$\bar{z} = \frac{120}{40} = 3 \text{ ft}$$

The resultant therefore must be an upward force of 40 lb intersecting a line parallel to and 3 ft in front of the x axis.

The magnitude of the moments of the forces with respect to the z axis is as follows:

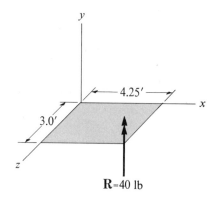

$$\Sigma M_z = R\bar{x} = 40(\bar{x}) = (40)(2) \qquad (30)(4) = \quad 80 \qquad 120$$
$$(60)(4) \qquad (30)(1) \qquad \underline{240} \qquad \underline{30}$$
$$320 \qquad 150$$
$$\underline{-150}$$
$$170 \text{ ft-lb}$$

$$\bar{x} = \frac{170}{40} = 4.25 \text{ ft}$$

In order to have the proper moment with respect to the z axis and the x axis, the resultant must be 4.25 ft to the right of the z axis and 3.0 ft in front of the x axis as shown on the sketch in Fig. 2–15b.

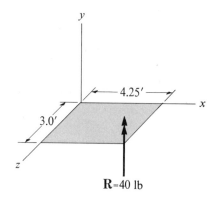

R=40 lb   **Fig. 2-15b**

Example 2-10   Determine the resultant of the four parallel forces in Fig. 2–16a.

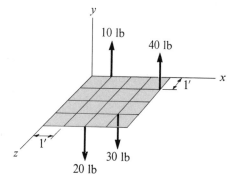

Fig. 2-16a

Solution: The forces of the system can be tabulated thus:

$$
\begin{array}{cc}
\uparrow & \downarrow \\
10 & 20 \\
\underline{40} & \underline{30} \\
50 & 50 \\
\underline{-50} & \\
\mathbf{R} = \quad 0 &
\end{array}
$$

However, for this system of forces, the resultant may be a couple. The summation of moments of the forces with respect to the z axis is

$$
\mathbf{C}_z = (20)(2) \quad (10)(1) = \quad
\begin{array}{cc}
40 & 10 \\
\underline{90} & \underline{160} \\
130 & 170 \\
 & \underline{-130} \\
 & 40 \text{ ft-lb}
\end{array}
$$
$$(30)(3) \quad (40)(4)$$

The summation of moments of the forces with respect to the x axis is

$$
\mathbf{C}_x = (40)(1) \quad (30)(3) = \quad
\begin{array}{cc}
40 & 90 \\
 & \underline{80} \\
\underline{} & 170 \\
40 & \underline{-40} \\
 & 130 \text{ ft-lb}
\end{array}
$$
$$(20)(4)$$

$$C = (C_x^2 + C_z^2)^{1/2} = (130^2 + 40^2)^{1/2} = 136.2 \text{ ft-lb}$$

The resultant therefore is a couple as shown in Fig. 2-16b.

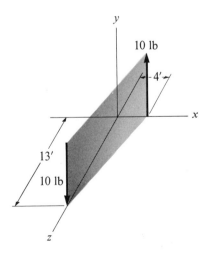

Fig. 2-16b

Example 2-11 The 60-lb force **R** in Fig. 2–17a is the resultant of five forces, four of which are shown. Determine the unknown force and show it on a sketch with respect to the origin.

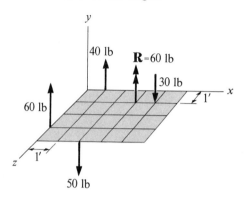

Fig. 2-17a

Solution: Assume the unknown force **F** acts vertically upward. Then from **R** = ΣF_y,

$$\uparrow \quad \uparrow \quad \downarrow$$
$$60 = 40 + 50$$
$$\quad\quad 60 \quad 30$$
$$\quad\quad\ F$$

and algebraically,

$$60 = 100 + F - 80$$

and

$$F = 140 - 100 = 40 \text{ lb} \uparrow$$

By the principle of moments, that is $Rx = \Sigma M_z$, the horizontal distance x from the z axis to the parallel plane of the force is found as follows:

$$3(60) = 40(1) + 50(2)$$
$$\quad\quad\ 40(x) \quad 30(4)$$

and algebraically,

$$180 = 40 + 40x - 100 - 120$$

Then,

$$40x = 180 + 100 + 120 - 40 = 360$$
$$x = \frac{360}{40} = 9 \text{ ft}$$

Since x is found to be positive with an assumed counterclockwise moment of the 40-lb upward acting force, x is to the right of the z axis. Also, in a similar manner, $Rz = \Sigma M_x$, and thus

$$60(1) = 60(3) + 30(1)$$
$$\quad\quad\ 40(z) \quad 50(4)$$

and algebraically,

$$60 = 180 + 40z - 30 - 200$$

Then,

$$40z = 60 + 30 + 200 - 180 = 110$$

$$z = \frac{110}{40} = 2.75 \text{ ft}$$

Since z is found to be positive with an assumed clockwise moment of the 40-lb upward acting force, z is in front of the x-axis. Fig. 2-17b indicates the position of force **F** with respect to the origin.

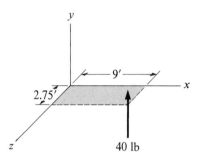

Fig. 2-17b

PROBLEMS

2-55. Determine the resultant of the noncoplanar, parallel force system in Fig. P 2–55 and show it on a sketch.

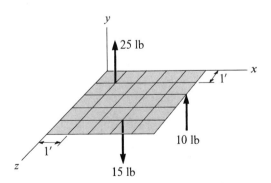

Fig. P 2-55

2-56. Given the parallel, noncoplanar force system in Fig. P 2–56, determine the resultant completely and show it on a sketch of the system.

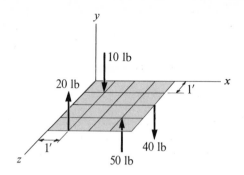

Fig. P 2-56

2-57. Determine the resultant of the parallel force system shown in Fig. P 2–57 and locate it on a sketch.

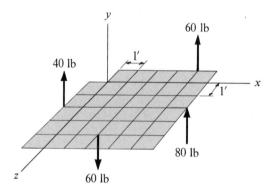

Fig. P 2-57

2-58. Determine the resultant of the noncoplanar force system in Fig. P 2–58 and show it on a sketch of the system.

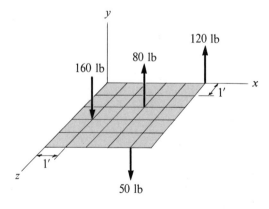

Fig. P 2-58

2-59. Determine the resultant of the force system in Fig. P 2–59 and show it on a sketch.

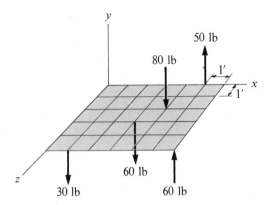

Fig. P 2-59

2-60. Determine completely the resultant of the noncoplanar force system represented in Fig. P 2–60. Show the resultant on a sketch of the system.

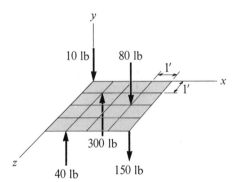

Fig. P 2-60

2-61. Determine completely the resultant of the parallel, noncoplanar force system in Fig. P 2–61 and show it on a sketch of the system.

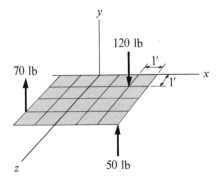

Fig. P 2-61

2-62. Determine completely the resultant of the noncoplanar force system in Fig. P 2–62 and show it on a sketch of the system.

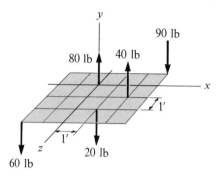

Fig. P 2-62

2-63. Determine the resultant of the noncoplanar force system in Fig. P 2–63 and show it on a sketch.

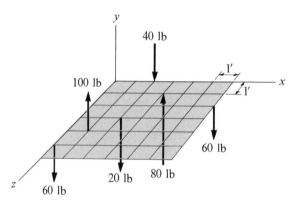

Fig. P 2-63

2-64. The 40-lb force **R** in Fig. P 2–64 is the resultant of four forces, three of which are shown. Determine the fourth force and show it on a sketch.

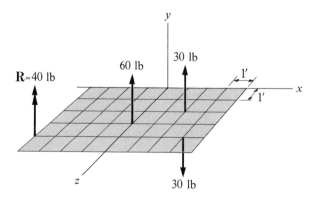

Fig. P 2-64

2-65.   In Fig. P 2–65, the 100 ft-lb couple indicated is the resultant of five parallel, noncoplanar forces, four of which are shown. Determine the unknown force and show it on a sketch.

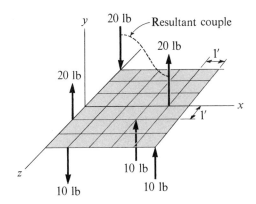

Fig. P 2-65

2-8   RESULTANT OF A SYSTEM OF COUPLES IN SPACE

The resultant of any number of couples in space is a couple. To prove this, refer to Fig. 2–18. Since the forces of any two couples can be made the same by changing the distance between the forces of the couples, one force of each couple can be made equal, opposite, and collinear with

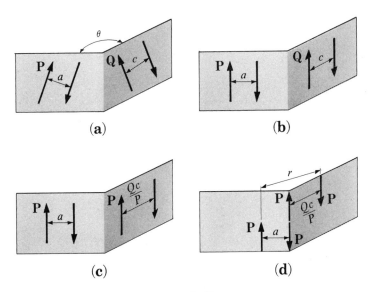

Fig. 2-18

the other by rotation or translation. The two remaining forces will be equal, opposite, and noncollinear, forming a resultant couple. In a similar fashion the resultant of these two couples can be combined with any other couple until a final resultant couple is obtained.

For example, refer to the two couples Pa and Qc in Fig. 2–18a, which make an angle θ with each other. The force Q can be changed in magnitude to P, providing the distance between the forces of the couple is changed to Qc/P. Thus the original magnitude of the couple Qc is not changed, since $(P)(Qc/P) = Qc$. The length of the arm of this couple is found by using the cosine law for a triangle:

$$r = \left[a^2 + \frac{(Qc)^2}{P^2} - \left(\frac{2aQc}{P}\right)\cos\theta\right]^{1/2}$$

The steps in the transformations of the two couples are shown in Figs. 2–18b, 2–18c, and 2–18d.

When θ is 90°, $\cos\theta$ is zero and the equation above becomes

$$r = \left(a^2 + \frac{(Qc)^2}{P^2}\right)^{1/2}$$

and the magnitude of the resultant couple becomes

$$C_R = Pr = [(Pa)^2 + (Qc)^2]^{1/2}$$

That is, the magnitude of the moment of the resultant couple is the square root of the sum of the squares of the magnitudes of the moments of component couples. The sense of rotation is determined by the sign of the algebraic summation.

PROBLEMS

2-66.   Determine the resultant of the two couples in Fig. P 2–66.

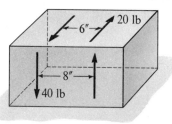

Fig. P 2-66

2-67.   The block in Fig. P 2–67 is subjected to a pair of couples as shown. By means of the transformations of a couple, replace the two couples by a single couple having the same external effect on the body.

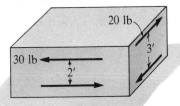

Fig. P 2-67

2-68. In Fig. P 2–68, the couples lie in the *yz* and *xz* planes. By means of the transformations of a couple, replace the two couples by a single couple which will have the same external effect.

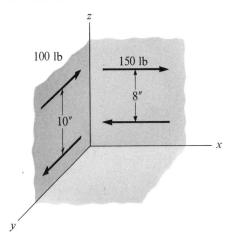

Fig. P 2-68

2-69. Determine completely the resultant of the two couples shown in Fig. P 2–69. One couple is in the *xz* and the other in the *yz* plane.

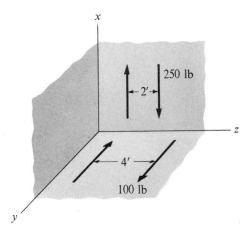

Fig. P 2-69

2-70. Determine the resultant of the three couples shown in Fig. P 2–70.

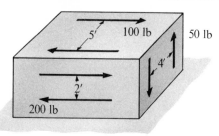

Fig. P 2-70

2-71. Determine the resultant of the three couples shown in Fig. P 2–71.

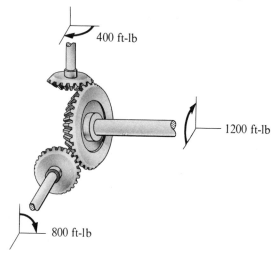

Fig. P 2-71

2-72. Determine the resultant of the two couples shown in Fig. P 2–72.

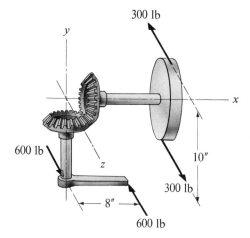

Fig. P 2-72

2-9   N O N C O P L A N A R ,   N O N C O N C U R R E N T , N O N P A R A L L E L   S Y S T E M   O F   F O R C E S

The resultant of a system of noncoplanar, nonconcurrent, nonparallel forces may be a force, a couple, or a force and a couple.

In order to find the resultant of such a system of forces, each force may be resolved into a force at some point, such as the origin of a system of coordinate axes, and a couple, as discussed in Sec. 1–12. This will result in a system of concurrent forces and a system of couples in various planes. The resultant of the concurrent system of forces is a force through the point of concurrence and may be obtained as discussed in Sec. 2–6. The resultant of the system of couples is a couple which may be obtained as discussed in Sec. 2–8. The resultant then may be a force and a couple.

If the resultant couple and force lie in the same plane, they may be combined to form a single force. If the summation of the concurrent forces is zero, the resultant may be a couple. If the resultant couple also becomes zero, the body will be in equilibrium.

2-10   S U M M A R Y

The possible resultants, other than zero, of various force systems have been discussed in this chapter. For a concurrent system of forces, coplanar or noncoplanar, the resultant can be only a force. For a parallel system of forces, either coplanar or noncoplanar, and for a coplanar, nonconcurrent system of forces, the resultant may be a force or a couple. However the resultant cannot be a force and a couple, since a coplanar force and couple may be further reduced to a single force.

In case the summations of forces in the x and y directions are zero, the resultant is not a force but may be a couple. If the summation of the moments of the forces with respect to any axis is not zero, the resultant is a couple and it is equal to the algebraic sum of the moments of the forces.

For a noncoplanar, nonparallel, nonconcurrent system of forces, the resultant may be a force, a couple, or a force and a couple. The resultant will be a force and a couple when the plane of the resultant couple is at right angles to the plane of the resultant force, since for this situation the force and couple cannot be reduced to a single force.

R E V I E W   P R O B L E M S

2-73.   Three coplanar forces, **S**, **T**, and **U**, are shown in Fig. P 2–73. When $S = 15$ lb, $T = 10$ lb, and $U = 12$ lb, determine the resultant **(a)** graphically, by means of the parallelogram law, (b) graphically, by means of the triangle law, and (c) algebraically.

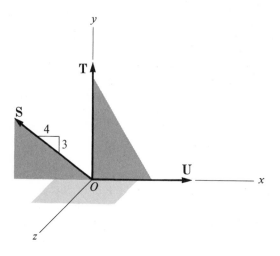

Fig. P 2-73

2-74. Determine the resultant force **R** of the forces **S**, **T**, and **U** shown in Fig. P 2–73 algebraically when $S = 10$ lb, $T = 9$ lb, and $U = 5$ lb.

2-75. The truss shown in Fig. P 2–75 is acted upon by three forces. Find the resultant algebraically and locate it with respect to point D.

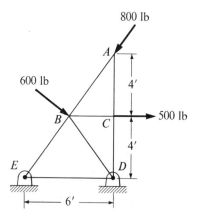

Fig. P 2-75

2-76. A dam, of which Fig. P 2–76 is a cross-section, weighs 150 pcf and is 20 ft long. Determine the resultant of the weight of the dam, the horizontal 90,000-lb water pressure, and the 112,000-lb uplift force, and locate the resultant with respect to the toe of the dam.

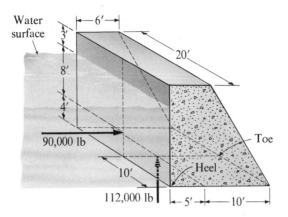

Fig. P 2-76

2-77. Determine the resultant of the four forces shown in Fig. P 2–77 and locate it with respect to point *C*.

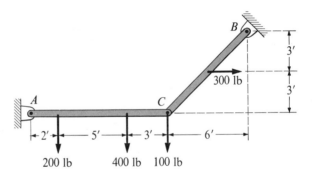

Fig. P 2-77

2-78. The resultant of the coplanar forces acting on the car in Fig. P 2–78 is a horizontal force **R** of 150 lb acting to the left at the center of gravity. Determine the magnitudes of the forces R_1, R_2, and **F** (total).

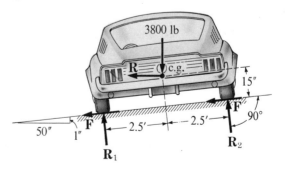

Fig. P 2-78

2-79. The 2000-lb boat shown in Fig. P 2–79 carries a 400-lb motor and a 700-lb cargo. Determine the resultant of the five forces shown and locate it with respect to point *G*.

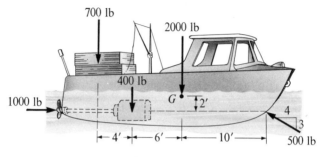

700 lb

2000 lb

400 lb

1000 lb

G 2′

4
3

4′ 6′ 10′

500 lb

Fig. P 2-79

2-80. Determine the resultant of the coplanar force system acting on the tractor in Fig. P 2–80.

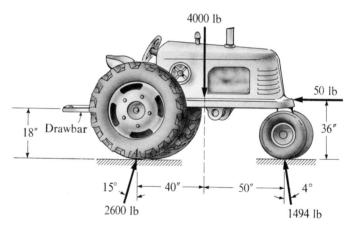

4000 lb

50 lb

18″ Drawbar

36″

15°

40″ 50″ 4°

2600 lb

1494 lb

Fig. P 2-80

2-81. In Problem 2-80, what will be the reaction at point *A* of the driving wheel if the drawbar pull is 1000 lb?

3

Equilibrium of Force Systems

3-1 INTRODUCTION

When a force system acting on a body has no resultant, the body on which the system of forces acts is in equilibrium. For coplanar force systems *the graphic requirements for equilibrium are that both the force and string polygons must close.* For any type of force system *the algebraic requirements for equilibrium are that the sum of the forces in any direction must equal zero and that the algebraic sum of the moments of the forces about any axis must be equal to zero.* By means of these conditions, either algebraic or graphic, it is possible to determine one or more unknown forces acting on a body which is in equilibrium, depending on the type of force system involved. The graphic solution is more easily applied to coplanar force systems than to noncoplanar force systems. The algebraic solution is applicable to all types of force systems.

3-2 GRAPHIC CONDITIONS OF EQUILIBRIUM

In Chapter 2 it was found that the resultant of an unbalanced force system in a plane is either a force or a couple. Also it was shown that if the resultant is a force, the magnitude and sense of this resultant force are represented by the closing side of the force polygon, and that if the resultant is a couple, the two forces of the couple act along the first and last strings of the string polygon. Therefore if the force polygon closes with no side representing the resultant (i.e., only the original forces form the closed polygon), the resultant may be a couple but it cannot be a force. However, if the string polygon closes also, that is, if the first and last strings along which the two forces of the couple would act are collinear, the two forces cancel each other and thus there is no resultant couple. Therefore if (1) the force polygon closes, and (2) the string polygon closes, the coplanar force system will be in equilibrium.

3-3 ALGEBRAIC CONDITIONS OF EQUILIBRIUM

The two conditions stated above for the graphic solution for equilibrium may be expressed algebraically. Fig. 3–1 shows a closed polygon. If the forces are projected on any two axes taken at right angles to each other, they will form two collinear force systems in the directions of these axes.

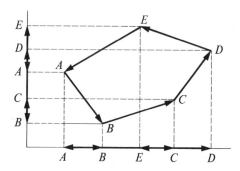

Fig. 3-1

These projections (components) form closed force polygons also, and therefore their vector sums are equal to zero. Since these projections were made in any direction, it may be stated that the algebraic sum of the components of the forces in any direction is equal to zero.

If the string polygon closes also, the resultant cannot be a couple, since the first and last strings of the polygon will be collinear and therefore the algebraic sum of the moments of these two forces about any moment center will be zero.

3-4 FREE-BODY DIAGRAM

Before the equations of equilibrium can be applied correctly to a system of forces acting on any body, all forces acting on the body must be accurately shown. For this purpose it is necessary to construct a free-body diagram.

A free-body diagram is a sketch of a body completely free from all other bodies, representing as forces the action of all removed bodies on the free body. Each force in a free-body diagram should be labeled either with its known magnitude or with a letter designation if its magnitude is unknown. The slope of all forces not horizontal or vertical should be indicated. The sense of unknown forces may be assumed when not exactly known. The correct sense of an unknown force will be determined from the solution of its magnitude. If it is assumed as a positive value and the solution indicates it to be negative, or vice versa, its correct sense will be opposite to that assumed.

In order to draw a free-body diagram correctly, the force or forces exerted on a body by each type of connection or contact must be shown. Some ways in which the action of bodies or connections can be represented by a force or forces on a free-body diagram when the bodies or connections are removed are illustrated in Table 2.

Example 3-1   Body *AB* in Fig. 3–2a is acted upon by a 500-lb force at *E* and body *CD* by a 100-lb force at *C*. Draw a free-body diagram of each of the two bodies.

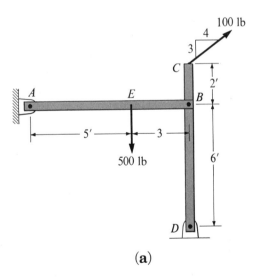

Fig. 3-2   **(a)**

Table 2

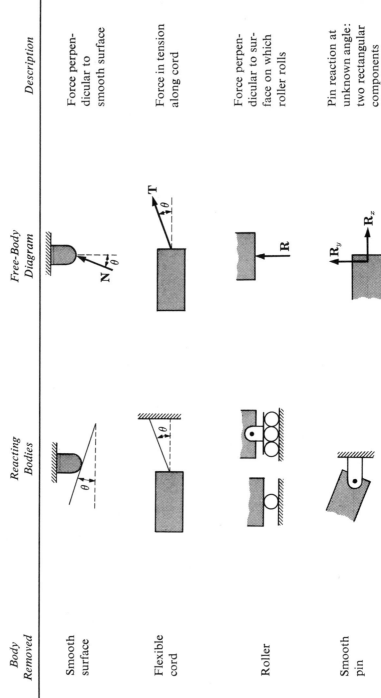

Body Removed	Reacting Bodies	Free-Body Diagram	Description
Smooth surface			Force perpendicular to smooth surface
Flexible cord			Force in tension along cord
Roller			Force perpendicular to surface on which roller rolls
Smooth pin			Pin reaction at unknown angle: two rectangular components

Smooth bearing			Reaction perpendicular to shaft at unknown angle: two rectangular components
Ball and socket			Force on ball at unknown angle three rectangular components
Runner in smooth guide			Force perpendicular to guide or slot
Earth			Vertical force equal to weight, passing through center of gravity of body

Solution: Figures 3–2b and 3–2c are the two free-body diagrams. The pin reaction at B on body AB is assumed to be upward and to the right. The components of this reaction, B_x and B_y, represent the action of body CD on body AB. The force exerted by AB on body CD at the pin B has the same magnitude but acts in the opposite direction. Thus the same components are shown downward and to the left at B on member CD. The components at A and D may be taken in any direction, providing the angle between the components is always 90°. It is generally advisable to take the components at a pin connection parallel and perpendicular to the member, or horizontal and vertical.

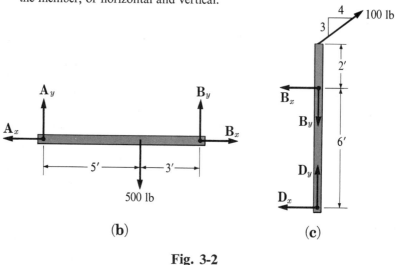

(b)   **(c)**

Fig. 3-2

Example 3-2   Body CD in Fig. 3–3a is acted upon by the 100-lb weight F, the body AB, and the cord CE. Draw a free-body diagram of body AB and one of body CD.

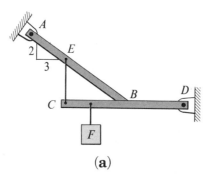

(a)   **Fig. 3-3**

Solution: Figs. 3–3b and 3–3c show the two free bodies. The cord *CE* is always shown in tension, since a cord cannot take compression. The force at *B* is perpendicular to and against the surface of contact. The components at *A* and *D* are taken vertically and horizontally.

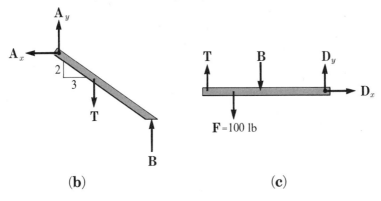

(b)   (c)

Fig. 3-3

PROBLEMS

Note: All pins and surfaces are to considered smooth (without friction) in the following problems.

3-1.   Member *AB* in Fig. P 3–1 weighs 300 lb. Draw a free-body diagram of *AB*.

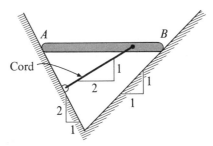

Fig. P 3-1

3-2.   Draw a free-body diagram of bar *CDE* in Fig. P 3–2. Neglect the weights of the members.

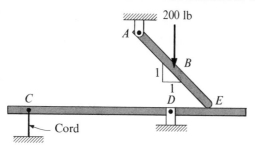

Fig. P 3-2

3-3. Draw a free-body diagram of each of the two cylinders in Fig. P 3–3. Cylinder *A* weighs 50 lb and *B* weighs 30 lb.

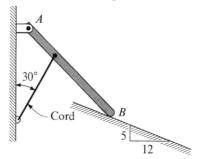

Fig. P 3-3

3-4. Draw a free-body diagram of the 100-lb homogeneous bar *AB* shown in Fig. P 3–4. The bar *AB* rests upon a smooth inclined plane at *B*.

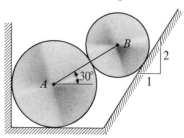

Fig. P 3-4

3-5. Draw a free-body diagram of the beam *AB* in Fig. P3–5. Neglect the weight of the member.

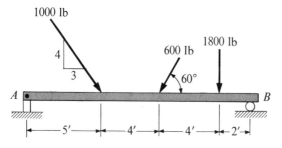

Fig. P 3-5

3-6. Draw a free-body diagram of bar *CEG* in Fig. P 3–31.

3-7. Draw a free-body diagram of bar *AC* shown in Fig. P 3–32.

3-8. Draw a free-body diagram of bar *AB* and pulley shown in Fig. P 3–34. Consider the bar and pulley as one body.

3-5 CONCURRENT, COPLANAR FORCE SYSTEM

The resultant of a concurrent, coplanar force system acting on a body is a single force acting through the point of concurrence. To ensure equilibrium of such a force system, the resultant force acting on the body must be zero. To ensure a zero resultant, the magnitude of the sum of the forces in any direction must be equal to zero.

Consider the force system in Fig. 3–4. If the magnitude of the sum of

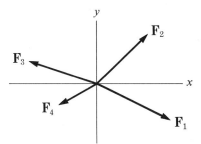

Fig. 3-4

the *x* components of the forces of the system equals zero, the resultant, if any, can only act perpendicular to the *x* axis. However, if the magnitude of the sum of the *y* components of the forces of the system also is equal to zero, the resultant must be zero and the body is in equilibrium.

Therefore a system of coplanar, concurrent forces is in equilibrium if the forces of the system satisfy the following equations:

$$\Sigma F_x = 0 \qquad \Sigma F_y = 0 \tag{3-1}$$

A second set of equations which satisfy the conditions of equilibrium is:

$$\Sigma F_x = 0 \qquad \Sigma M_A = 0 \tag{3-2}$$

where the *x* and *y* axes intersect at the point of concurrence of the forces and the point *A* is any point not on the *y* axis.

A third set of equations which will ensure equilibrium is:

$$\Sigma M_A = 0 \qquad \Sigma M_B = 0 \tag{3-3}$$

where the line joining *A* and *B* does not pass through the point of concurrence of the forces of the system.

Since there are only two independent equations which ensure equilibrium in each instance, this force system can contain not more than two unknowns.

For a collinear force system Eq. 3-1 reduces to one equation:

$$\Sigma F_x = 0$$

where the x axis is parallel to the collinear forces. Also Eqs. 3-2 and 3-3 can be reduced to the equation

$$\Sigma M_A = 0$$

where A is not on the action line of the collinear forces. Only one unknown can be determined when a collinear force system is in equilibrium.

Example 3-3 A 260-lb homogeneous sphere rests against the smooth crossarms as shown in Fig. 3–5a. Determine the reactions of the arms at points A and B on the sphere.

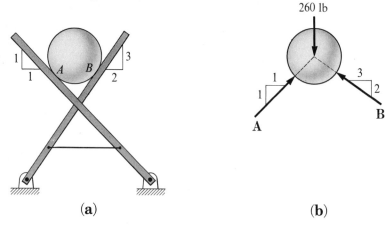

(a)   (b)

Fig. 3-5

Solution: Since the arms are smooth, the reactions of the arms on the sphere at A and B will be perpendicular to the arms, with their lines of action passing through the center of the sphere. This is a concurrent, coplanar system of forces for which there are two independent equations. Since there are only two unknowns, forces **A** and **B**, they can be solved readily by use of the free-body diagram in Fig. 3–5b.

First resolve the two unknowns into their x and y components. Then by $\Sigma F_x = 0$,

$$0.707A - \left(\frac{3}{13^{1/2}}\right)B = 0$$

$$0.707A = \left(\frac{3}{13^{1/2}}\right)B \tag{3-4}$$

$\Sigma F_y = 0$ gives

$$0.707A + \left(\frac{2}{13^{1/2}}\right)B - 260 = 0 \qquad\qquad (3\text{-}5)$$

By substituting the value of $0.707A$ of Eq. 3–4 into Eq. 3–5,

$$\left(\frac{3}{13^{1/2}}\right)B + \left(\frac{2}{13^{1/2}}\right)B = 260$$

$$B = 260\left(\frac{13^{1/2}}{5}\right) = 187.5 \text{ lb} \quad \searrow\!\!\!\raisebox{1ex}{\scriptsize 3}_{\,2}$$

and

$$A = \left(\frac{3}{13^{1/2}}\right)\left(\frac{187.5}{0.707}\right) = 220.5 \text{ lb} \quad \nearrow\!\!\raisebox{1ex}{\scriptsize 1}_{\,1}$$

3-6 TWO-FORCE MEMBERS

If a body is held in equilibrium by only two forces, these forces must be collinear, equal, and opposite in sense. Such a body or member is referred to as a *two-force member*. If the two forces are not collinear and parallel, they must be concurrent and therefore have a resultant, as demonstrated by the parallelogram law. If they are parallel but not concurrent, they will form a couple. Thus the resultant will be zero and the body in equilibrium only when the two forces are equal, opposite in sense, and collinear.

Example 3-4 Determine the pin-reaction at B on member CB as shown in Fig. 3–6a.

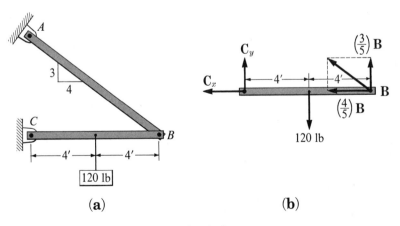

(a)   **(b)**

Fig. 3-6

Solution: Draw a free-body diagram of the member *CB* as shown in Fig. 3–6b. Since member *AB* is a two-force member, the reaction at *B* can be shown with its line of action in the direction *AB*. The vertical component of force **B** is (3/5)**B**. By the summation of moments about point *C*,

$$\left(\frac{3}{5}\right)B(8) - 120(4) = 0$$

$$\mathbf{B} = 480\left(\frac{5}{24}\right) = 100 \text{ lb} \quad \searrow_{3}^{4}$$

on member *CB*.

3-7   THREE-FORCE MEMBERS

If three coplanar, nonparallel forces acting on a body are in equilibrium, the forces must be concurrent. In order that the three forces shall be in equilibrium, the resultant of any two of the forces must be equal, opposite, and collinear with the third force. However, the resultant of the two forces will have the same line of action as the third force only if the two forces intersect on the action line of the third force, in which case the three forces are concurrent. This fact often can be used advantageously to locate the point of intersection of three forces that hold a body in equilibrium and thus provide a simpler solution to such a problem. This is demonstrated in the example below.

Example 3-5   A ladder carrying a 200-lb man rests against a wall as shown in Fig. 3–7a. If the vertical wall is considered smooth (frictionless), determine the reactions on the ladder at points *A* and *B*.

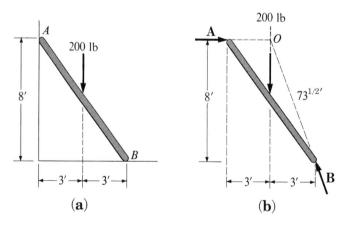

(a)   (b)

Fig. 3-7

Solution: Since the wall at A is smooth, the reaction of the wall on the ladder at A is horizontal and to the right. This force will intersect the weight vector at point O. Since three forces in equilibrium and not parallel must intersect at a common point, the reaction vector at point B must pass through point O as shown in Fig. 3–7b. The solution can be obtained as follows:

A.   Algebraic Method

By $\Sigma F_y = 0$,

$$\left(\frac{8}{73^{1/2}}\right)B - 200 = 0$$

$$B = 200\left(\frac{73^{1/2}}{8}\right) = 214 \text{ lb}$$

$\Sigma F_x = 0$ gives

$$A - \left(\frac{3}{73^{1/2}}\right)B = 0$$

$$A = 214\left(\frac{3}{73^{1/2}}\right) = 75 \text{ lb} \rightarrow$$

B.   Graphic Method

Construct a force polygon as shown in Fig. 3–7c. Use the 200-lb force C and the horizontal force A, and close with the force B at a slope of eight vertical to three horizontal (as determined from Fig. 3–7b).

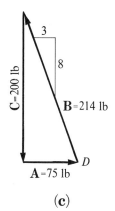

Fig. 3-7   **(c)**

The force B will intersect the horizontal force A at point D. Scaling off the two unknowns gives:

$$A = 75 \text{ lb} \rightarrow \qquad B = 214 \text{ lb}$$

PROBLEMS

3-9.   In Fig. P 3–9, the 150-lb sphere rests against the smooth walls as shown. Determine the reactions of the walls at A and B on the sphere.

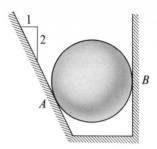

Fig. P 3-9

3-10. Determine the tensile force in the cable *D* of the cable system shown in Fig. P 3–10.

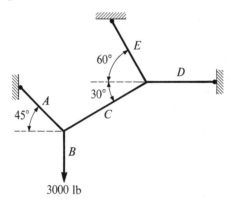

Fig. P 3-10

3-11. In Fig. P 3–11, the 100-lb cylinder rests against the smooth plane and is held in position by means of a cord. Determine all unknown forces acting on the cylinder.

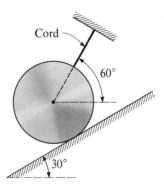

Fig. P 3-11

3-12. Determine the stresses in members *AC* and *BC* of the truss shown in Fig. P 3–12.

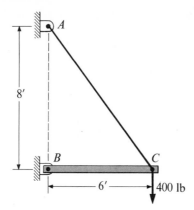

Fig. P 3-12

3-13. A flexible hoisting rope passes over a sheave at joint C of the truss shown in Fig. P 3–13. Find the resulting stresses in members AC and BC.

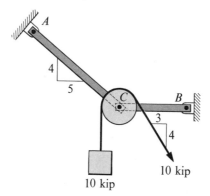

Fig. P 3-13

3-14. Using the three-force and two-force principles, determine the reactions at A and D on the truss shown in Fig. P 3–14 resulting from the 600-lb neon sign supported at point C.

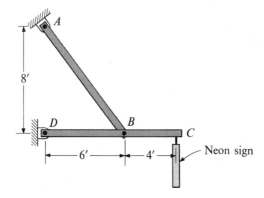

Fig. P 3-14

3-15. The pin-connected member in Fig. P 3–15 supports the rail for a traveling crane. Using the two-force and three-force principles, determine the reactions at *A* and *D* on the truss due to the 100-lb load of the rail.

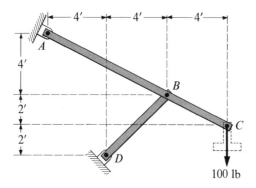

100 lb   **Fig. P 3-15**

3-16. Using the three-force principle, determine the force **F** required to start to tip the homogeneous block of concrete shown in Fig. P 3–16 about the corner *C* (assuming it does not slide) and the reacting force at *C*. The weight *W* of the concrete block is 10,000 lb.

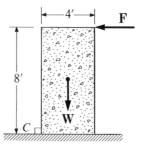

Fig. P 3-16

3-17. A man exerts a horizontal force **P** against a 120-lb log to hold it from sliding down an icy incline which may be considered frictionless, as shown in Fig. P 3–17. Determine all the unknown forces acting on the log.

Fig. P 3-17

3-18. A man is lowering a 100-lb box of merchandise down an inclined chute into a truck at a uniform speed, as shown in Fig. P 3–18. If the inclined chute is frictionless, determine the magnitudes of all the unknown forces acting on the box.

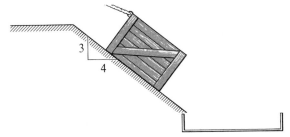

Fig. P 3-18

3-19. In Fig. P 3–19, the 160-lb sphere rests against the smooth walls as shown. Determine the reaction of the wall at point *A* on the sphere.

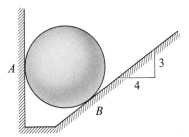

Fig. P 3-19

3-20. In Fig. P 3–20, a 100-lb sphere rests against the smooth plane and is acted upon by a 60-lb force as shown. Determine all the unknown forces acting on the sphere.

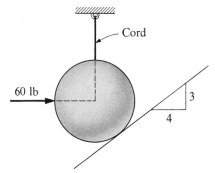

Fig. P 3-20

3-21. In Fig. P 3–21, a 100-lb sphere rests against the smooth plane. The sphere is held in position by means of the flexible cable. Determine all unknown reactions acting on the sphere.

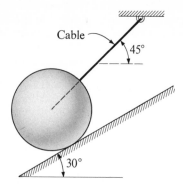

Fig. P 3-21

3-22. Determine the tensile stresses in the cords *A*, *B*, *C*, and *D* supporting the 100-lb weight in Fig. P 3–22.

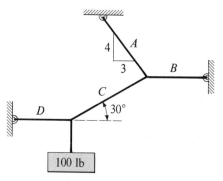

Fig. P 3-22

3-23. The two steel shafts crated in a wooden box, as shown in Fig. P 3–23, have the same diameter and weigh 100 lb each. Neglecting friction at all contact surfaces, determine the reaction of the lower shaft against the side of the crate at *A*.

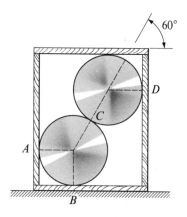

Fig. P 3-23

3-8 NONCONCURRENT, COPLANAR FORCE SYSTEM

A. Algebraic Method

A nonconcurrent, coplanar system of forces is in equilibrium if the forces of the system satisfy the equations

$$\Sigma F_x = 0 \qquad \Sigma F_y = 0 \qquad \Sigma M_A = 0$$

where A is any point in the plane of the forces. If the magnitude of the sum of the moments of the forces of the system with respect to point A is zero, where AB is any axis perpendicular to the plane of the forces, the resultant cannot be a couple. Also, if a resultant force exists, it must pass through point A. If the magnitudes of the sums of the x and y components of the forces of the system are both equal to zero, there cannot be a resultant force and therefore the system of forces will be in equilibrium.

A second complete set of equations of equilibrium for this system is

$$\Sigma M_A = 0 \qquad \Sigma M_B = 0 \qquad \Sigma F_x = 0$$

where the x axis is not perpendicular to the line AB.

A third complete set of equations of equilibrium for this system is

$$\Sigma M_A = 0 \qquad \Sigma M_B = 0 \qquad \Sigma M_C = 0$$

where points A, B, and C are not collinear. The proof that these equations will ensure equilibrium is left to the student.

Regardless of which set of equations is used, there are only three independent equations of equilibrium and therefore this force system can have no more than three unknowns.

When all the forces of the system are parallel, one of the equations from each of the sets above can be dropped. For example, if the parallel forces act in the y direction, the equation $\Sigma F_x = 0$ in the first set will give no usable information.

Example 3-6 Determine the horizontal and vertical components of the pin reactions at A and C of the pin-connected structure shown in Fig. 3–8a.

Solution: A free-body diagram of the entire structure, Fig. 3–8b, indicates there are four unknowns, while this force system has only three independent equations of equilibrium. An additional free-body diagram of member AB, Fig. 3–8c, adds two more unknowns (a total of six) and yields three more independent equations (a total of six). Thus the two free-body diagrams have six independent equations and six unknowns, which ensures that all unknowns can be solved.

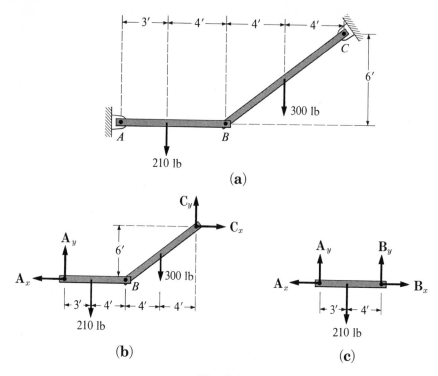

Fig. 3-8

From the free-body diagram of AB:

$$\Sigma M_B = 0$$

$$7A_y - 840 = 0$$

$$A_y = \frac{840}{7} = 120 \text{ lb} \uparrow \text{ on } ABC$$

From the free-body diagram of the entire structure:

$$\Sigma M_C = 0$$

$$120(15) + 6A_x - 210(12) - 300(4) = 0$$
$$1800 + 6A_x - 2520 - 1200 = 0$$
$$6A_x = 1920$$
$$A_x = 320 \text{ lb} \leftarrow \text{ on } ABC$$

$$\Sigma F_x = 0$$

$$C_x = 320 \text{ lb} \rightarrow \text{ on } ABC$$

$$\Sigma F_y = 0$$

$$C_y + 120 = 510$$

$$C_y = 390 \text{ lb} \uparrow \text{ on } ABC$$

Example 3-7 Determine the horizontal and vertical components of the pin reactions at B on members AB and BC of the pin-connected structure in Fig. 3–8a if an additional 500-lb force is added to the pin at B as shown in the free-body diagram in Fig. 3–9a.

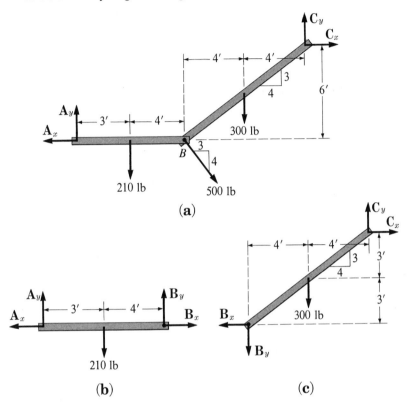

Fig. 3-9

Solution: Since it is not known what portion of the additional 500-lb force added to the pin at B is supported by the member AB and what portion is supported by the member BC, it cannot be stated that the components of the reaction at B on the two members are equal in magnitude but opposite in direction. Therefore, it is first necessary to determine the components of the reactions at A and C, and then solve for the components of the reaction at B on the two members.

Summing moments about C on the free-body diagram in Fig. 3–9a gives

$$6A_x + 15A_y - 210(12) - 300(4) - 400(8) - 300(6) = 0$$
$$6A_x + 15A_y = 8720$$

From the free-body diagram in Fig. 3–9b, $\Sigma M_B = 0$ gives

$$7A_y - 210(4) = 0$$

$$\mathbf{A}_y = \frac{840}{7} = 120 \text{ lb} \uparrow \text{ on } AB$$

Therefore,

$$6A_x + 15(120) = 8720$$

$$6A_x = 6920$$

$$\mathbf{A}_x = 1153.3 \text{ lb} \leftarrow \text{ on } AB$$

By the summation of forces in Fig. 3–9b the components of the reaction at B on member AB can be obtained. Thus,

$$\Sigma F_x = 0$$

$$B_x - 1153.3 = 0$$

$$\mathbf{B}_x = 1153.3 \text{ lb} \rightarrow \text{ on } AB$$

$$\Sigma F_y = 0$$

$$B_y + 120 - 210 = 0$$

$$\mathbf{B}_y = 90 \text{ lb} \uparrow \text{ on } AB$$

By the summation of forces in Fig. 3–9a the components of the reaction at C can be obtained. Thus,

$$\Sigma F_x = 0$$

$$C_x + 300 - 1153.3 = 0$$

$$\mathbf{C}_x = 853.3 \text{ lb} \rightarrow \text{ on } BC$$

$$\Sigma F_y = 0$$

$$C_y + 120 - 510 - 400 = 0$$

$$\mathbf{C}_y = 790 \text{ lb} \uparrow \text{ on } BC$$

Now by the summation of forces in Fig. 3–9c the components of the reaction at B on member BC can be obtained. Thus,

$$\Sigma F_x = 0$$

$$B_x - 853.3 = 0$$

$$\mathbf{B}_x = 853.3 \text{ lb} \leftarrow \text{ on } BC$$

$$\Sigma F_y = 0$$

$$B_y + 300 - 790 = 0$$

$$\mathbf{B}_y = 490 \text{ lb} \downarrow \text{ on } BC$$

In this problem it is found that the x and y components of the reactions at B are not of the same magnitude on members AB and BC because of the addition of the 500-lb force at B.

Example 3-8 Determine the reactions at A and B on the beam in Fig. 3–10a. Neglect the weight of the beam.

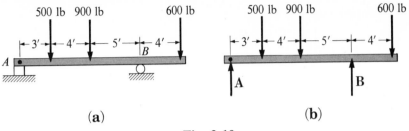

(a)   (b)

Fig. 3-10

Solution: The free-body diagram of the beam is shown in Fig. 3–10b. Since this is a parallel, coplanar system of forces, two independent equations apply, as follows:

$$\Sigma M_B = 0$$

$$12A + 600(4) - 900(5) - 500(9) = 0$$

$$12A = 4500 + 4500 - 2400 = 6600$$

$$A = \frac{6600}{12} = 550 \text{ lb} \uparrow$$

$$\Sigma F_y = 0$$

$$B + 550 - 500 - 900 - 600 = 0$$

$$B = 2000 - 500 = 1450 \text{ lb} \uparrow$$

B. Graphic Method

Problems involving nonconcurrent, coplanar force systems in equilibrium can be solved by the graphic method as outlined in Sec. 3–2. A graphic method of solution, making use of force and string polygons for a typical problem, is demonstrated below. In this problem all the forces are known except the two end reactions. The action line of the right reaction is known, since a roller is used at this point, as indicated in Fig. 3–11a. Only a point on the action line of the left reaction is known, since the left end is pin-connected. The unknown elements, therefore, are the magnitude and direction of the reaction at the left end and the magnitude of the reaction at the right end. The space diagram and the force and string polygon are shown in Figs. 3–11a and 3–11b. The forces **AB**, **BC**, and **CD** are drawn first to represent the three known forces. Since the magnitude of force **DE** is unknown, the location of E is not known, but it must lie on a vertical line through D. The rays OA, OB, OC, and OD are drawn from any point O, after which the space diagram is constructed as shown in Fig. 3–11a. Since the point M is the only known point on the action line of force **ea** (**EA**), the space diagram must be started at this point. The strings oa, ob, oc, and od are drawn as shown. Since the string oe must

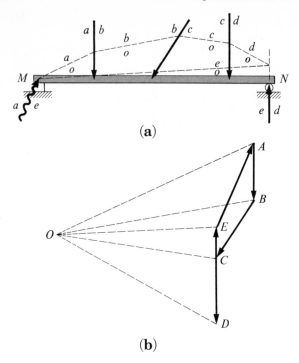

(a)

(b)   Fig. 3-11

intersect *od* on **de** and must also intersect *oa* on **ea**, its position is determined. The ray OE must be parallel to the string *oe*. Therefore E is the point of intersection of a vertical line through D and a line through O parallel to *oe*. Then the left reaction is represented in magnitude and in direction by **EA**, and the right reaction in magnitude by **DE**.

PROBLEMS

3-24. Determine the components of the pin reaction at A on member AD in Fig. P 3–24. Neglect the weights of the members.

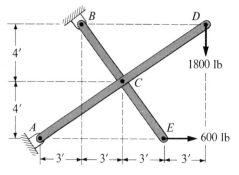

Fig. P 3-24

3-25. Body *D* in Fig. P 3–25 weighs 210 lb. The weights of the other members may be neglected. Determine the components of the pin reaction at *B* on member *AB*.

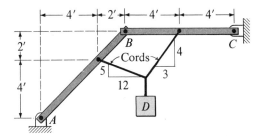

Fig. P 3-25

3-26. The motor-driven windlass rotates the frame in Fig. P 3–26 about the pin at *B*. When the frame is in the fixed position shown, determine the pin reaction at *C* on member *BD*. Neglect the weights of all members.

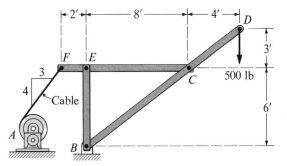

Fig. P 3-26

3-27. The weights of the members of the pin-connected structure shown in Fig. P 3–27 may be neglected. Determine the reaction at *B* on member *ABC*.

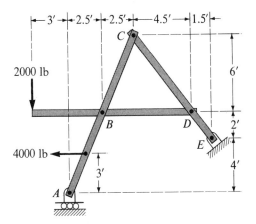

Fig. P 3-27

3-28. In Fig. P 3–28, the 500-lb weight *B* is fastened to a rope which passes over the frictionless pulley *A* and is attached to the member *CD*. Determine the components of the pin reactions at *C* and *E* on member *ACE*. Neglect the weights of all members.

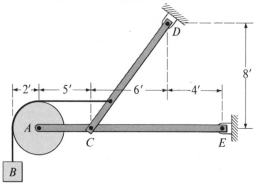

Fig. P 3-28

3-29. In the pin-connected structure shown in Fig. P 3–29, the weights of all members may be neglected. Determine the pin reaction at *A* on *AC*.

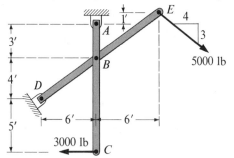

Fig. P 3-29

3-30. The frame in Fig. P 3–30, rotated by a motor-driven windlass, is used to dip logs into a vat of hot creosote. In the position shown, the logs weigh 800 lb. Determine the pin reaction at *F* on member *BFG*. Neglect the weights of all members.

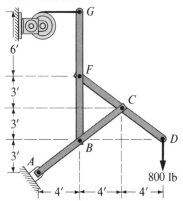

Fig. P 3-30

3-31. In the pin-connected structure of Fig. P 3–31, determine the components of the pin reaction at *B* on member *BEF*. Neglect the weights of all members.

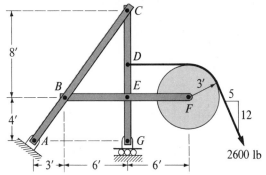

Fig. P 3-31

3-32. Determine the horizontal and vertical components of the reaction of the pin at *B* on member *ABC* of Fig. P 3–32. Neglect the weights of the members.

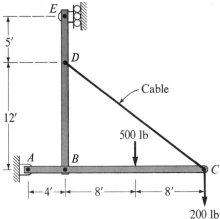

Fig. P 3-32

3-33. Determine the horizontal and vertical components of the reaction at pin *D* on member *AG* of the pin-connected frame shown in Fig. P 3–33. Neglect weights of all members.

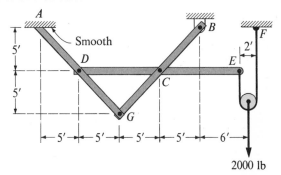

Fig. P 3-33

3-34. In Fig. P 3–34, the body *F* weighs 500 lb. The weights of all other members may be neglected. Determine the horizontal and vertical components of the pin reactions at *C* and *E* on member *CD*.

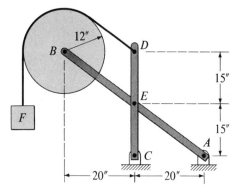

Fig. P 3-34

3-35. Determine the tension in cable *AB* and the reaction on the pin at *C* for the crane shown in Fig. P 3–35. Neglect the weight of beam *BC*.

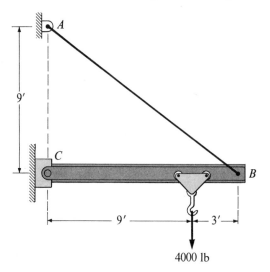

4000 lb   **Fig. P 3-35**

3-36. Determine the reactions at supports *A* and *E* of the beam shown in Fig. P 3–36.

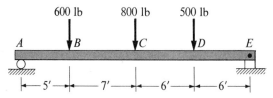

Fig. P 3-36

3-37. In Fig. P 3–37, find the reactions at supports *A* and *E*.

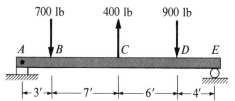

Fig. P 3-37

3-38. In Fig. P 3–38, determine the magnitude of force **P** that will be required to lift the 500-lb timber *AB* from its supporting platform, assuming that the rope and pulley are connected to the timber so that the timber remains horizontal.

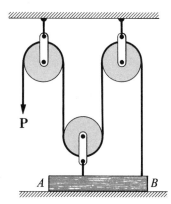

Fig. P 3-38

3-39. Find the reactions produced by loads *B* and *C* at supports *A* and *D* of the beam shown in Fig. P 3–39.

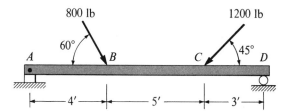

Fig. P 3-39

3-40. Determine the reactions at *A* and *E* of the beam shown in Fig. P 3–40.

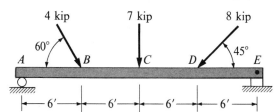

Fig. P 3-40

3-41. In Fig. P 3–41, bodies A and B remain at rest on smooth planes. Body A weighs 100 lb. Determine the weight of body B and all other unknown forces acting on it. Neglect friction in the pulley C.

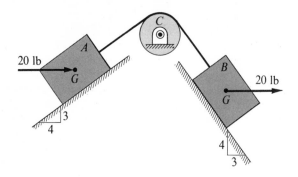

Fig. P 3-41

3-42. Determine the equilibrant of the parallel force system shown in Fig. P 3–42 with respect to point A.

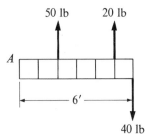

Fig. P 3-42

3-43. The vertical bar shown in Fig. P 3–43 is held in equilibrium by the three forces shown and two forces acting along the lines ab and cd. Determine the magnitudes and senses of the two unknown forces. Neglect the weight of the member.

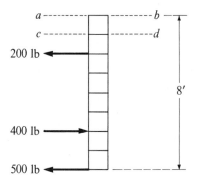

Fig. P 3-43

3-44.   Solve Problem 3-36 graphically.

3-45.   Solve Problem 3-37 graphically.

3-46.   Solve Problem 3-39 graphically.

3-47.   Solve Problem 3-40 graphically.

3-9   T R U S S E S

A truss is a rigid body composed of a number of members fastened together at their ends. Trusses are often used in roof and bridge construction. In this discussion, trusses in which members, loads, and reactions are all in the same plane are considered.

In determining the stresses in members of a truss, the following assumptions are made:

1.   The members of the truss are joined together at their ends by smooth pins.
2.   The loads and reactions act only at the joints.
3.   The weights of the members are neglected.

In actual practice, when the weights of the members cannot be neglected, the weight of each member is divided in half, and half the weight is applied at each end of the member at the joint.

It follows from these assumptions that each member of a truss is a two-force member, and therefore that the stress, or total internal force, in each member is directed along the member. When the applied load tends to stretch the member as indicated in Fig. 3–12a, the internal force is called a *tensile stress*. When the load tends to shorten the member as indicated in Fig. 3–12b, the internal force is called a *compressive stress*.

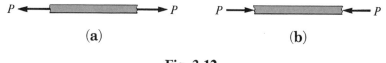

(a)   **(b)**

Fig. 3-12

It is suggested that all unknown stresses be considered as tensile stresses. Then, if the value of the unknown stress is calculated as a positive value, it will be a tensile stress, but if it is calculated as a negative value, it will be a compressive stress.

In the algebraic calculation of stresses in members of a truss, by use of the equations of equilibrium, two methods may be employed, namely, the method of joints and the method of sections.

3-10 METHOD OF JOINTS

By the method of joints, a joint is isolated as shown in Fig. 3–13a by cutting all members that are attached to a common pin, thus forming a free-body diagram of the pin-connected joint. Such free bodies are shown in Figs. 3–13b, c, and d. The force system is concurrent and

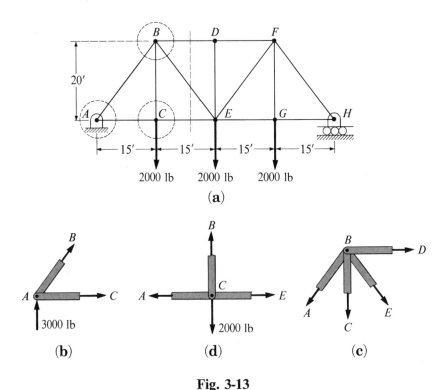

Fig. 3-13

coplanar. Since such a system has two independent equations of equilibrium, only two unknowns can be involved. Therefore, in determining the stresses in the members of a truss by the method of joints, the equations of equilibrium must be applied to the joints in such a manner that not more than. two unknown stresses are involved at each joint. Thus, if the stress in a member near the center of the truss is desired, it is usually necessary to start at one end of the truss and determine the equilibrium of successive joints until the joint is reached which involves the particular member in the center of the truss. The following problem illustrates the method of joints.

Example 3-9   Determine the stress in member BE of Fig. 3–13a.

Solution: A free-body diagram of joint B, Fig. 3–13c, indicates four unknowns. Thus, the stress cannot be determined directly by starting with this free body. Joint A has two unknowns, as shown in Fig. 3–13b. Therefore, using

$\Sigma F_y = 0$

$$\left(\frac{4}{5}\right)AB + 3000 = 0$$

$$AB = 3000\left(-\frac{5}{4}\right)$$

$$\mathbf{AB} = -3750 \text{ lb} = 3750 \text{ lb } C \text{ (compression)}$$

The stress is compression since it was assumed in tension and the calculated value is negative.

$\Sigma F_x = 0$

$$AC + \left(\frac{3}{5}\right)AB = 0$$

$$AC + \left(\frac{3}{5}\right)-3750 = 0$$

$$AC = 2250 \text{ lb } T \text{ (tension)}$$

With the stress in AB determined, three unknowns still remain at joint B. Therefore, one of the unknowns must be determined from another joint. Going next to joint C, two unknowns, **BC** and **CE**, remain. Using the free-body diagram of joint C, Fig. 3–13d,

$\Sigma F_y = 0$

$$BC - 2000 = 0$$

$$\mathbf{BC} = 2000 \text{ lb } T$$

Now, using the free-body diagram of joint B, which now has only two unknowns, **BD** and **BE**, remaining,

$\Sigma F_y = 0$

$$\left(\frac{4}{5}\right)BE + 2000 + \left(\frac{4}{5}\right)AB = 0$$

$$\left(\frac{4}{5}\right)BE + 2000 + \left(\frac{4}{5}\right)\left(-3750\right) = 0$$

$$\left(\frac{4}{5}\right)BE = 3000 - 2000 = 1000 \text{ lb}$$

$$\mathbf{BE} = 1000\left(\frac{5}{4}\right) = 1250 \text{ lb } T$$

Note that if an error were made in computing the stress in member AB, the resulting stress in BE would also be in error.

3-11 METHOD OF SECTIONS

In order to determine stresses in members of a truss by the method of sections, a section is isolated as shown in Fig. 3–14, where the truss in Fig. 3–13a has been cut into two parts. The resulting free-body diagram, Fig. 3–14, should have not more than three unknowns, since the force system acting on the body is a coplanar, nonconcurrent, nonparallel system having only three independent equations of equilibrium. Therefore, whenever possible, a free body of a section is produced with only three unknowns. Occasionally, sections may be cut with more than three unknowns. In such cases additional free bodies of sections or joints may be necessary for the solution of the additional unknowns.

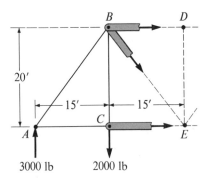

Fig. 3-14

By the proper choice of moment centers or of directions of summation of forces, each of the three unknowns often may be determined by a single equation, thus avoiding the use of simultaneous equations. The following example demonstrates the method of sections.

Example 3-10   Determine the stresses in members BD, BE, and CE of the truss shown in Fig. 3–13a.

Solution: The members BD, BE, and CE are cut, and a free-body diagram of the left part of the truss is produced, as shown in Fig. 3–14. The stress in member BD will be solved first. Since BE and CE intersect at E, moments of the forces will be taken with respect to point E, thereby eliminating the two unknown forces in BE and CE from the moment equation.

$$\Sigma M_E = 0$$

$$20BD + 3000(30) - 2000(15) = 0$$

$$20BD = 30,000 - 90,000 = -60,000$$

$$\mathbf{BD} = -3000 \text{ lb} = 3000 \text{ lb } C$$

Now, since **BE** is the only unknown force that has a component in the vertical direction, a summation of the forces in the vertical direction gives

$\Sigma F_y = 0$

$$\left(\frac{4}{5}\right)BE + 2000 - 3000 = 0$$

$$\left(\frac{4}{5}\right)BE = 3000 - 2000 = 1000$$

$$BE = 1000\left(\frac{5}{4}\right) = 1250 \text{ lb } T$$

Finally, by taking moments of the forces with respect to point B, the stress in member CE is determined.

$\Sigma M_B = 0$

$$20CE - 3000(15) = 0$$

$$20CE = 45{,}000$$

$$CE = \frac{45{,}000}{20} = 2250 \text{ lb } T$$

Example 3-11   Determine the stresses in members BC, BF, and EF of the pin-connected truss in Fig. 3–15a.

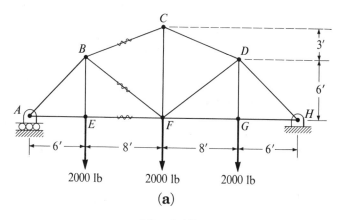

(a)

Fig. 3-15

Solution: Cut the three members BC, BF, and EF, and draw the free-body diagram as shown in Fig. 3–15b. There are three unknowns, for which there are also three independent equations. Extend the line of action of the force in member BC until it intersects the extension of the line of action of the force in member AE at point O. The point of interesection O is 10 ft to the left of point A.

By the summation of moments about O, forces **BC** and **EF** are eliminated from the equation and **BF** can be obtained directly. By resolving

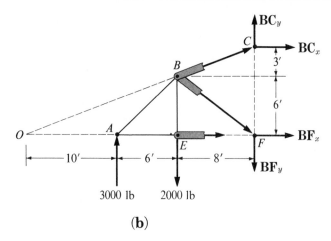

(b)

Fig. 3-15

the force **BF** into its components at point F, the moment of the horizontal component about point O becomes zero and the moment of the vertical component, which is the moment of force **BF** about point O, becomes

$$\left(\frac{3}{5}\right)BF(24) + 2000(16) - 3000(10) = 0$$

$$14.4BF = -2000$$

$$\mathbf{BF} = \frac{-2000}{14.4} = 138.8 \text{ lb } C$$

By the summation of moments about F, forces **BF** and **EF** are eliminated from the equation and **BC** can be obtained directly. By resolving **BC** into its components at point C, the y component has no moment about F and the moment of **BC** about F becomes

$$\left(\frac{8}{73^{1/2}}\right)BC(9) + 3000(14) - 2000(8) = 0$$

$$\frac{72BC}{73^{1/2}} = -26,000$$

$$\mathbf{BC} = -26,000\left(\frac{73^{1/2}}{72}\right) = 3090 \text{ lb } C$$

By the summation of moments about B, forces **BC** and **BF** are eliminated from the equation and **EF** can be obtained directly. Thus,

$$6EF - 3000(6) = 0$$

$$\mathbf{EF} = 3000 \text{ lb } T$$

Example 3-12 The diagonal members EG and DF in the center panel of Fig. 3–16a are designed to take tension only. For the loading indicated, determine which of these diagonals is in tension and the magnitude of the tensile stress.

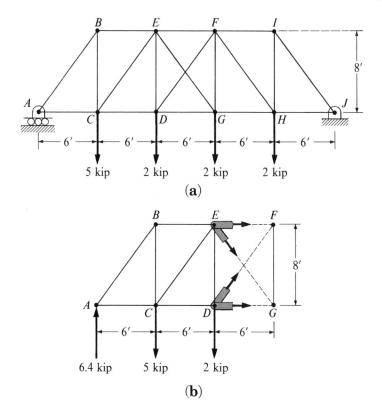

Fig. 3-16

Solution: By the summation of moments with respect to the right support J in Fig. 3–16a, the reaction at support A may be determined. Thus,

$$5A - 5(4) - 2(3) - 2(2) - 2(1) = 0$$

$$5A = 20 + 6 + 4 + 2 = 32$$

$$\mathbf{A} = 6.4 \text{ kip } \uparrow$$

Pass a vertical plane between E and F, cutting members EF, EG, DF, and DG, and draw the free-body diagram as shown in Fig. 3–16b. Assume the member DF in tension and sum the forces in the vertical direction. Thus, $\Sigma F_y = 0$ gives

$$\left(\frac{4}{5}\right)DF + 6.4 - 5 - 2 = 0$$

$$\left(\frac{4}{5}\right)DF = 0.6$$

$$\mathbf{DF} = 0.75 \text{ kip } T$$

The stress in member EG is zero since it cannot be in tension and does not take compression.

PROBLEMS

3-48. Determine the stresses in members *AB*, *DF*, and *DG* of the pin-connected truss in Fig. P 3–48.

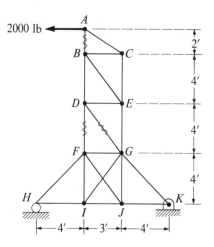

Fig. P 3-48

3-49. Determine the stresses in the members *EG*, *BC*, and *BD* of the coplanar, pin-connected truss in Fig. P 3–49.

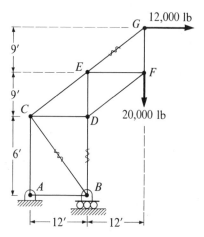

Fig. P 3-49

3-50. In the pin-connected truss in Fig. P 3–50, determine the stresses in the members *BE*, *CE*, and *FJ*.

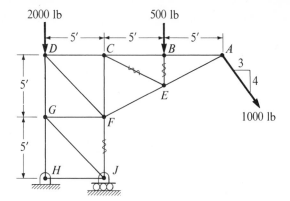

Fig. P 3-50

3-51. Determine the stresses in members *CD*, *CF*, and *EJ* of the truss in Fig. P 3–51.

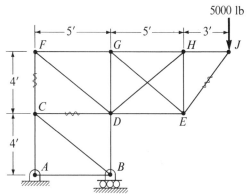

Fig. P 3-51

3-52. Determine the stresses in members *CD*, *CH*, and *DH* of the pin-connected truss in Fig. P 3–52.

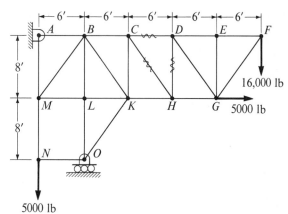

Fig. P 3-52

3-53. Determine the stresses in members AB, BD, and BC of the pin-connected roof truss in Fig. P 3–53.

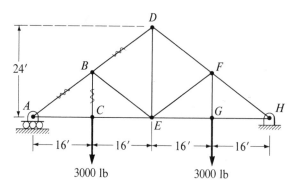

Fig. P 3-53

3-54. Determine the stresses in members BC and BI of the pin-connected bridge truss in Fig. P 3–54.

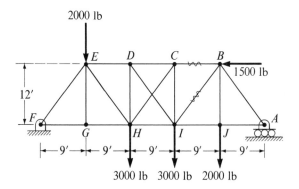

Fig. P 3-54

3-55. Determine the stresses in members DE and GD of the pin-connected truss in Fig. P 3–55.

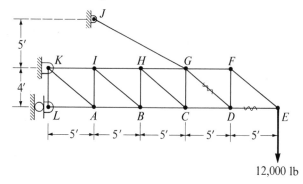

Fig. P 3-55

3-56. Determine the stresses in members *BH*, *AH*, and *BG* of the pin-connected cantilevered truss shown in Fig. P 3–56.

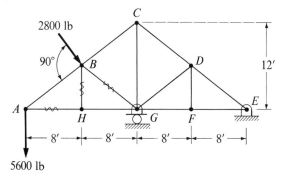

Fig. P 3-56   5600 lb

3-57. Determine the stresses in members *CF*, *CH*, and *BC* of the pin-connected truss shown in Fig. P 3–57.

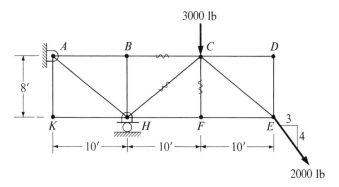

Fig. P 3-57

3-58. Determine the stresses in members *BD*, *CD*, and *CE* of the pin-connected Warren truss in Fig. P 3–58.

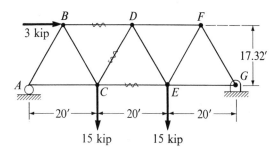

Fig. P 3-58   15 kip   15 kip

3-59. The truss shown in Fig. P 3–59 supports three signal lights, each weighing 200 lb. Assuming the vertical columns take equal horizontal thrust, determine the stresses in members *BC*, *BL*, and *ML* of this pin-connected truss. The resultant wind load is applied horizontally at point *N*.

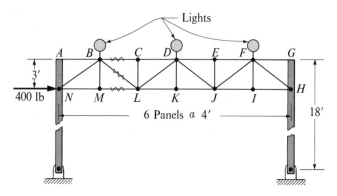

Fig. P 3-59

3-60. The pin-connected truss in Fig. P 3–60 is one of number spaced at 10 ft intervals, which support a concrete walkway weighing 100 lb per horizontal square foot. Determine the stresses in members *AD*, *AC*, and *BC*.

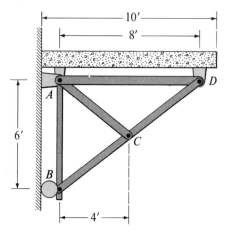

Fig. P 3-60

3-12   GRAPHIC ANALYSIS OF TRUSSES

The graphic method of analyzing a truss can give accuracies to within 1 or 2 per cent. First the external reactions are determined either by an algebraic or a graphic solution. Then the stresses in members can be determined from force polygons drawn for the various joints. Since each joint of the truss is held in equilibrium by a concurrent force system, only two unknown forces can be determined from each force polygon. Therefore a joint with only two members must be selected for the first polygon.

The subsequent force polygons must be chosen for those joints for which only two unknown stresses exist in each case. In the process, the force polygon for each joint is superimposed on the force polygons that have been constructed previously in order that no member be duplicated in the composite diagram. This diagram is called a *stress diagram*, and it shows the stresses in the individual members and the external loads and reactions.

The procedure for drawing a stress diagram is illustrated in the following example.

Example 3-13 Determine by the graphic method the stresses in the members of the truss shown in Fig. 3–17a.

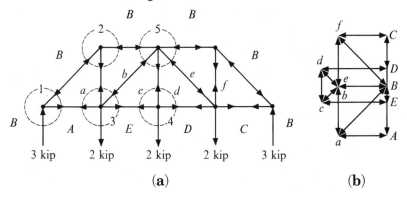

(a)   (b)

Fig. 3-17

Solution: Bow's system of notation is used, so that each force or stress can be properly identified. A slight variation of the notation given in Chapter 2 is employed: Capital letters are used when referring to external forces (as in Fig. 3–17b, the force polygon) *or to the spaces around them* (as in Fig. 3–17a, the stress diagram), while lower-case letters are reserved for indicating both the internal forces of the force polygon *and* the spaces around them in the stress diagram.

The stress diagram is started by drawing the force polygon for the external forces and reactions. This force polygon is represented by the forces **AB, BC, CD, DE,** and **EA.** Next a joint with only two members or unknowns must be selected in Fig. 3–17a. In this case the joint at the left end of the truss, joint 1, is used. The unknown stresses are **Ba** and **aA.**

The analysis and plotting of external and internal forces at each joint proceeds in a clockwise direction. At joint 1, **AB** has already been plotted in the force polygon, Fig. 3–17b. Next **Ba** is plotted in the force polygon: it must be at 45° with the horizontal and must run through point *B*. Lying tip to tail with **AB**, it has a direction downward to the left; its magnitude has not yet been determined. Then **aA** is drawn in the force polygon horizontally as required and intersecting **Ba** at *a*; lying tip to tail with **Ba**, its direction is found to be to the right. This gives the closed polygon *BaA*, and the magnitudes of **Ba** and **aA** become evident through scaling. Since **Ba** is plotted downward to the left, it is in compression, and since **Aa** is plotted to the right, it is in tension. The direction plotted is always with respect to the joint involved. The two unknowns at joint 1 have now been completely solved.

Next, consider joint 2 (upper left), which now has only two unknowns, since **Ba** has been found. Starting with the known force **aB** and going clockwise, **Bb** is plotted in the force polygon horizontally to the left (compression), and **ba** vertically downward (tension), intersecting **aB** at *a*.

Now joint 3 can be considered, since only two unknowns remain at this joint. Starting with the known stress **ab** and going clockwise, **bc** is plotted downward to the left (compression), and **cE** to the right (tension), intersecting **EA** at *E*. **EA** and **Aa** close the force polygon.

The next joint is number 4 at the center of the lower chord. Starting with the known stress **Ec**, **cd** is plotted upward (tension), and **dD** is plotted to the right (tension), intersecting **DE** at *D*.

When joint 5 is considered, it is found that three of its stresses are known from analysis of previous joints, leaving only **Be** and **ed** as unknowns about this joint. Since the truss is loaded symmetrically, these stresses in the members of the right half of the truss will be the same as their corresponding duplicates in the left half. When this symmetry does not exist, it will be necessary to continue plotting the joints as was done for the left half of the truss.

PROBLEMS

3-61. Determine the stresses in all members of the truss in Fig. P 3–53 using the graphic method.

3-62. Determine the stresses in all members of the truss in Fig. P 3–54 using the graphic method.

3-63. Determine the stresses in all members of the truss in Fig. P 3–56 using the graphical method.

3-64. Determine the stresses in all members of the truss in Fig. P 3–57 using the graphic method.

3-13 EQUILIBRIUM OF CONCURRENT FORCES IN SPACE

The resultant of a concurrent force system in space is a single force through the point of concurrence. Therefore this force system is in equilibrium if the magnitude of the resultant force is zero. The equations of equilibrium which will ensure a zero resultant are:

$$\Sigma F_x = 0 \qquad \Sigma F_y = 0 \qquad \Sigma F_z = 0$$

Any resultant force would have a component in the $x, y,$ or z direction. Therefore if no such components exist in these directions, the force system is in equilibrium.

Alternative sets of equations of equilibrium for the concurrent force system in space can be used by replacing one or more of the force equations by a corresponding number of moment equations. Since it would be difficult to remember all restrictions necessary for the selection of such additional moment axes, it is recommended that another axis be chosen if a redundant equation should appear.

Example 3-14 A 1000-lb load in Fig. 3–18 is supported by three struts, $AD,$ $BD,$ and $CD.$ The struts are connected at points $A, B, C,$ and D by ball and socket joints. Determine the total stress in each of the struts.

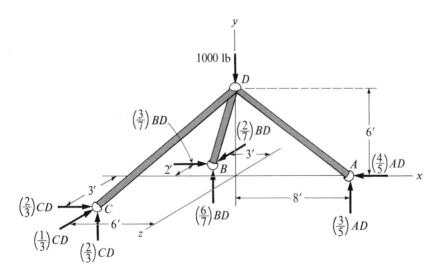

Fig. 3-18

Solution: Each of the struts is a two-force member. Therefore, the force in each can be expressed in terms of its three components. The length of each strut is

$$AD = (8^2 + 6^2 + 0)^{1/2} = 10$$

$$BD = (3^2 + 6^2 + 2^2)^{1/2} = 7$$

$$CD = (6^2 + 6^2 + 3^2)^{1/2} = 9$$

Adding the components in the x, y, and z directions gives

$$\Sigma F_x = 0: \qquad -0.8AD + \left(\frac{3}{7}\right)BD + \left(\frac{6}{9}\right)CD = 0 \qquad \text{(3-6)}$$

$$\Sigma F_y = 0: \qquad 0.6AD + \left(\frac{6}{7}\right)BD + \left(\frac{6}{9}\right)CD = 1000 \qquad \text{(3-7)}$$

$$\Sigma F_z = 0: \qquad \left(\frac{2}{7}\right)BD - \left(\frac{3}{9}\right)CD = 0 \qquad \text{(3-8)}$$

Solving Eqs. 3–6 and 3–7 simultaneously,

$$-2.4AD + \left(\frac{9}{7}\right)BD + \left(\frac{18}{9}\right)CD = 0$$

$$2.4AD + \left(\frac{24}{7}\right)BD + \left(\frac{24}{9}\right)CD = 4000$$

$$\overline{\left(\frac{33}{7}\right)BD + \left(\frac{42}{9}\right)CD = 4000}$$

Adding Eq. 3–8 $\qquad \left(\frac{28}{7}\right)BD - \left(\frac{42}{9}\right)CD = 0$

gives $\qquad\qquad \overline{\left(\frac{61}{7}\right)BD \qquad\qquad = 4000}$

$$\mathbf{BD} \qquad\qquad = 459 \text{ lb } C$$

and

$$\left(\frac{3}{9}\right)CD = \left(\frac{2}{7}\right)459$$

$$\mathbf{CD} = 394 \text{ lb } C$$

Also,

$$0.8AD = \left(\frac{3}{7}\right)459 + \left(\frac{2}{3}\right)394 = 460$$

$$\mathbf{AD} = 575 \text{ lb } C$$

Example 3-15 Block W in Fig. 3–19(a) weighs 1000 lb and is supported by the three cables. Determine the stress in each of the three cables.

Solution: The force system contains three unknowns, which can be determined from the three equations of equilibrium for a concurrent system of forces in space. Let the x, y, and z components of the total stress in each cable be applied at the respective supports. Assume all stresses to be tensile, as shown in the free-body diagram, Fig. 3–19b.

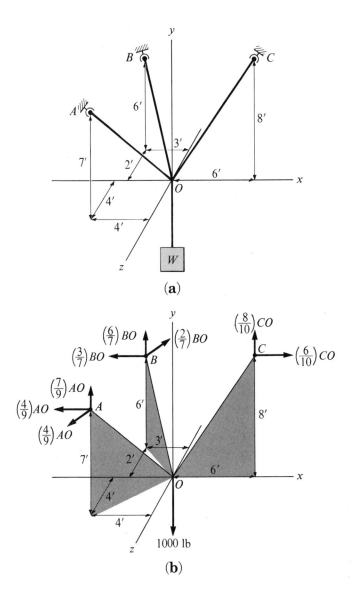

Fig. 3-19

The length of each of the three cords is as follows:

$$AO = (4^2 + 7^2 + 4^2)^{1/2} = 9$$
$$BO = (3^2 + 6^2 + 2^2)^{1/2} = 7$$
$$CO = (6^2 + 8^2 + 0)^{1/2} = 10$$

By the equation of equilibrium

$$\Sigma F_x = 0: \qquad \left(\frac{4}{9}\right)AO + \left(\frac{3}{7}\right)BO - \left(\frac{6}{10}\right)CO = 0$$

$$\Sigma F_y = 0: \qquad \left(\frac{7}{9}\right)AO + \left(\frac{6}{7}\right)BO + \left(\frac{8}{10}\right)CO = 1000$$

$$\Sigma F_z = 0: \qquad \left(\frac{4}{9}\right)AO - \left(\frac{2}{7}\right)BO \qquad\qquad = 0 \qquad\qquad \text{(3-9)}$$

Solving these three equations simultaneously gives

$$\mathbf{AO} = 278 \text{ lb } T \qquad \mathbf{BO} = 433 \text{ lb } T \qquad \mathbf{CO} = 512 \text{ lb } T$$

Frequently the solution of simultaneous equations (three in this case) can be simplified by the use of one or more moment equations. For instance, if the equations

$$\Sigma M_{C_x} = 0 \qquad \text{and} \qquad \Sigma M_{C_z} = 0$$

are used, the unknown **CO** is eliminated and **AO** and **BO** can be solved with two simultaneous equations. For example,

$$\Sigma M_{C_x} = 0$$

$$\left(\frac{4}{9}\right)AO(1) + \left(\frac{7}{9}\right)AO(4) - \left(\frac{2}{7}\right)BO(2) - \left(\frac{6}{7}\right)BO(2) = 0$$

$$\left(\frac{32}{9}\right)AO - \left(\frac{16}{7}\right)BO = 0 \qquad\qquad \text{(3-10)}$$

$$\Sigma M_{C_z} = 0$$

$$\left(\frac{4}{9}\right)AO(1) + \left(\frac{7}{9}\right)AO(10) + \left(\frac{3}{7}\right)BO(2) + \left(\frac{6}{7}\right)BO(9) = 6000$$

$$\left(\frac{74}{9}\right)AO + \left(\frac{60}{7}\right)BO = 6000$$

Then,

$$BO = \frac{32(7)AO}{9(16)} \qquad \left(\frac{74}{9}\right)AO + \left(\frac{60}{7}\right)\frac{32(7)AO}{9(16)} = 6000$$

$$\frac{194AO}{9} = 6000$$

and

$$AO = 278 \text{ lb } T \quad BO = 433 \text{ lb } T \quad CO = 512 \text{ lb } T$$

It will be noted that Eq. 3–10 is the same as Eq. 3–9 multiplied by a factor of 8. Also, if moments are taken with respect to C_y, a redundant equation will appear. For example,

$$\Sigma M_{C_y} = 0$$

$$\left(\frac{4}{9}\right)\widehat{AO}(4) - \left(\frac{4}{9}\right)\widehat{AO}(10) + \left(\frac{2}{7}\right)\widehat{BO}(9) - \left(\frac{3}{7}\right)\widehat{BO}(2) = 0$$

$$\left(\frac{-24}{9}\right)AO + \left(\frac{12}{7}\right)BO = 0$$

or

$$\left(\frac{32}{9}\right)AO - \left(\frac{16}{7}\right)BO = 0$$

which is the same as Eq. 3–10 above.

PROBLEMS

3-65. In Fig. P 3–65, AB and AD are flexible cables in a horizontal plane and AE is a rigid member connected to the vertical wall at E by means of a ball and socket. Determine the stresses in members AB and AE.

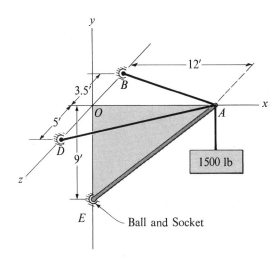

Fig. P 3-65

3-66. A shear-leg derrick, Fig. P 3–66, carries a load W of 2000 lb. The weights of the members may be neglected. AE and the vertical load are in the xy plane. Determine the stresses in legs BE and CE and in the cable AE.

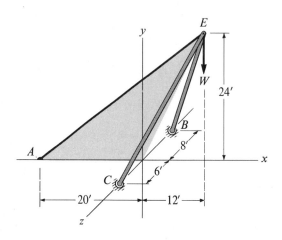

Fig. P 3-66

3-67. In the framework shown in Fig. P 3–67, all connections are made with a ball and socket, and the members AD, CD, and BD have their lower ends in the same horizontal plane. A horizontal force of 600 lb in the xy plane and acting parallel to the x axis is applied at D. Determine the stresses in members BD and AD.

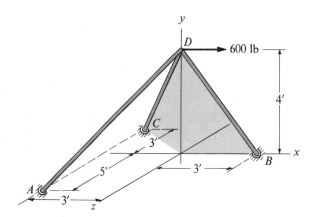

Fig. P 3-67

3-68. Compute the stresses in members AC and AD of the derrick shown in Fig. P 3–68. Neglect the weights of the members. Member AB has a ball and socket connection at B.

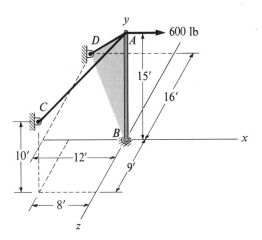

Fig. P 3-68

3-69. The members of the frame shown in Fig. P 3–69 are connected at their ends with ball and socket joints. Neglect the weights of the members. Determine the stress in member AD.

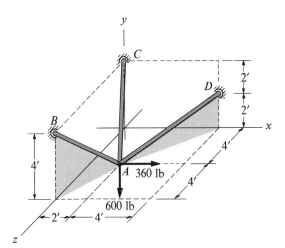

Fig. P 3-69

3-70. A 6000-lb weight is supported by three wires as shown in Fig. P 3–70. Determine the tension in each wire.

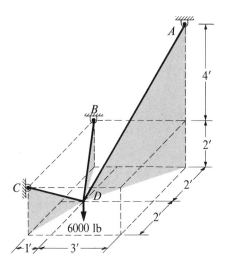

Fig. P 3-70

3-71. The members of the space frame in Fig. P 3–71 are connected at their ends with ball and socket joints. The weights of the members may be neglected. Determine the stress in member AB.

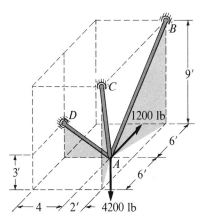

Fig. P 3-71

3-72. Body W in Fig. P 3–72 weighs 100 lb and is supported by three cords, AO, BO, and CO. Determine the tension in cord AO.

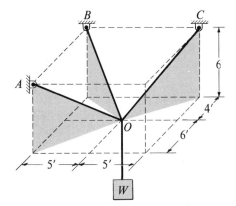

Fig. P 3-72

3-73. The balloon shown in Fig. P 3–73 is held down by three cables. If the upward force on the balloon is 3000 lb, determine the tension in cable AB.

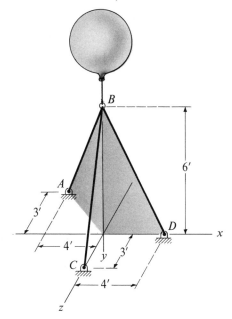

Fig. P 3-73

3-14   EQUILIBRIUM OF PARALLEL FORCES IN SPACE

A parallel system of forces in space is in equilibrium if the algebraic sum of the forces is zero and the algebraic sum of the moments of the forces with respect to each of two nonparallel axes is equal to zero, provided that neither of the axes is parallel to the forces of the system. If a set of rectangular axes is chosen with one of the axes (e.g., the y axis) parallel to the forces of the system, the equations of equilibrium may be written

$$\Sigma F_y = 0 \qquad \Sigma M_x = 0 \qquad \Sigma M_z = 0$$

If the forces of the system satisfy the equation $\Sigma F_y = 0$, the resultant, if any, cannot be a force. A resultant couple would have moments either about the x axis or the z axis or both. If the two moment equations are satisfied, there cannot be a resultant couple, and therefore the system of forces will be in equilibrium.

Example 3-16 The homogeneous wooden cross shown in Fig. 3–20a weighs 25 lb per linear foot and is supported as shown. All supports are applied at the center lines of the timbers. Determine the reactions at A, B, and C.

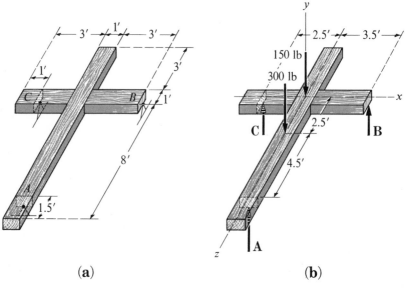

(a)   (b)

Fig. 3-20

Solution: For this system of forces, there are three independent equations. Since three unknowns are involved, their solutions can be determined readily.

The weight of the crossbeam is 6(25) = 150 lb, applied at the center as indicated in the free-body diagram in Fig. 3–20b. The weight of the main stem is 12(25) = 300 lb, applied 6 ft from each end. The reactions can be determined as follows:

$\Sigma M_{CB} = 0$

$$7A - 300(2.5) = 0$$
$$7A = 750$$
$$A = 107.1 \text{ lb} \uparrow$$

$\Sigma M_{B_z} = 0$

$$6C + 107.1(3.5) - 450(3.5) = 0$$
$$-6C = 375 - 1575$$
$$6C = 1200$$
$$C = 200 \text{ lb} \uparrow$$

$\Sigma F_y = 0$

$$B + 200 + 107.1 - 300 - 150 = 0$$
$$B = 142.9 \text{ lb} \uparrow$$

Example 3-17   The rectangular, horizontal steel plate shown in Fig. 3–21 weighs 100 lb per square foot and is supported in a horizontal position by vertical cables at points A, B, and C. Compute the tensions in the cables.

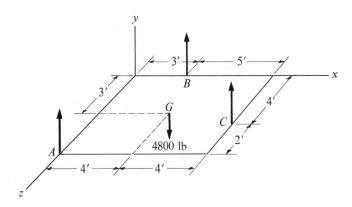

Fig. 3-21

Solution: The resultant weight of the plate passes through the mass center G of the plate. By writing two moment equations, one with respect to C_x and the other with respect to C_z, two equations containing the unknowns A and B can be solved simultaneously.

$\Sigma M_{C_z} = 0$: $2A$ $4B$ $2A - 4B = -4800$ **(3-11)**
$\quad\quad\quad\quad\quad\quad$ $4800(1)$

$\Sigma M_{C_z} = 0$: $8A$ $4800(4)$ $8A + 5B = 19,200$ (3-12)
                         $5B$

Multiplying Eq. 3–11 by 4 and changing signs gives:

$$-8A + 16B = 19,200$$

and adding $$8A + \ 5B = 19,200$$

gives $$\overline{ 21B = 38,400}$$ (3-13)

$$\mathbf{B} = 1830 \text{ lb} \uparrow$$

Then,

$$2A = -4800 + 7320 = 2520$$

$$\mathbf{A} = 1260 \text{ lb} \uparrow$$

$\Sigma F_y = 0$:

$$C + 1260 + 1830 = 4800$$

$$\mathbf{C} = 4800 - 3090 = 1710 \text{ lb} \uparrow$$

PROBLEMS

3-74. Determine all the unknown forces acting on the rigid horizontal frame shown in Fig. P 3–74. Neglect the weight of the frame.

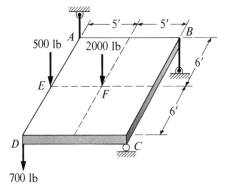

Fig. P 3-74

3-75. Determine all the unknown forces acting on the rigid horizontal frame in Fig. P. 3–75. Neglect the weight of the frame.

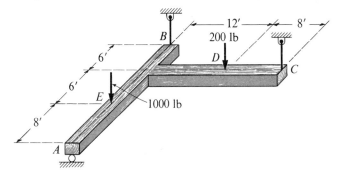

Fig. P 3-75

3-76. The circular plate shown in Fig. P 3–76 is supported by three vertical cables at *A*, *B*, and *C*. The 12,000-lb vertical force acts 6 in. from the center as shown, and the weight of the plate may be neglected. Determine the tension in each cable.

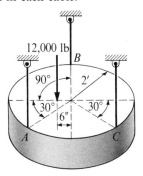

Fig. P 3-76

3-77. The horizontal plate *ABC* weighs 600 lb and is supported as shown in Fig. P 3–77. The center of gravity of the plate is located on the horizontal axis of symmetry from *C* to the front edge, and it is 2 ft from *C*. Determine all unknown forces acting on the plate.

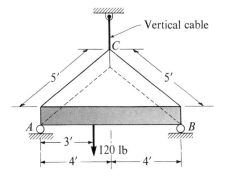

Fig. P 3-77

3-78. Determine all unknown forces acting on the rigid horizontal frame shown in Fig. P 3-78. Neglect the weight of the frame.

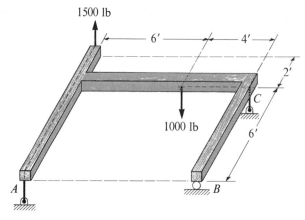

1500 lb

6'

4'

2'

C

1000 lb

6'

A

B

Fig. P 3-78

3-79. The homogeneous table in Fig. P 3-79 supports a stack of books weighing 50 lb and located as shown. Determine the upward reaction of the floor on legs A and B.

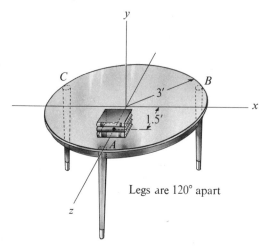

y

C

B

3'

x

1.5'

A

Legs are 120° apart

z

Fig. P 3-79

3-15 NONCONCURRENT, NONPARALLEL
SYSTEM OF FORCES IN SPACE

A system of nonconcurrent, nonparallel forces in space is in equilibrium if the magnitude of the algebraic sum of the components of the forces in each of three directions is equal to zero, and if the magnitude of the algebraic sum of the moments of the forces with respect to each of three perpendicular axes is equal to zero.

If the coordinate axes are taken for the axes of resolution and for the moment axes, the equations of equilibrium will be

$$\Sigma F_x = 0 \qquad \Sigma M_x = 0$$
$$\Sigma F_y = 0 \qquad \Sigma M_y = 0$$
$$\Sigma F_z = 0 \qquad \Sigma M_z = 0$$

If the three force equations are satisfied, the resultant cannot be a force but could be a couple in the yz, xz, or xy planes. However, if the three moment equations in the yz, xz, and xy planes are satisfied, the resultant cannot be a couple. Therefore, if all six equations are satisfied, the force system is in equilibrium.

Any of the force equations can be replaced by an additional moment equation, provided the moment axis is so selected that a redundant equation does not occur. Proper selection of moment axes becomes a matter of judgment and experience. Not more than six unknowns can be determined from one free-body diagram of a body in space, since there are only six independent equations of equilibrium.

Example 3-18 Determine the tension in the cables at C and E, and the reaction of the ball acting horizontally at A, on the body in Fig. 3-22a. Neglect the weight of the body.

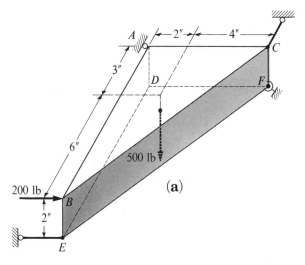

(a)

Fig. 3-22

Solution: The free-body diagram, Fig. 3-22b, shows the two known forces and six forces whose magnitudes are unknown. The equations of equilibrium are used in the following order:

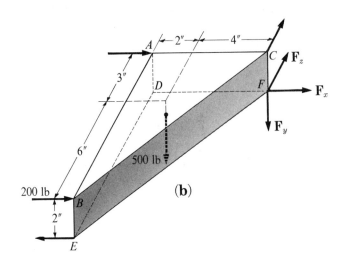

(b)

Fig. 3-22

$\Sigma M_{F_z} = 0$

$2C - 3(500) = 0$

$C = 750 \text{ lb } T$

$\Sigma M_{F_y} = 0$

$9E - 9(200) = 0$

$E = 200 \text{ lb } T$

$\Sigma M_{F_z} = 0$

$2A - 4(500) + 2(200) = 0$

$2A = 2000 - 400 = 1600$

$A = 800 \text{ lb } \rightarrow$

Example 3-19   A large homogeneous sign, weighing 400 lb, is hung on the side of a building as shown in Fig. 3–23a. The wind exerts a force of 100 lb on one side of the sign, and the vertical thrust at the hinges is taken by the hinge at B. Determine the components of the reactions at B and D on the sign and the tension in the cable AC.

Solution: Construct a free-body diagram of the sign as shown in Fig. 3–23b. There are six unknowns, and for this type of force system there are six independent equations.

Assume the coordinate axes to have their origin at D. Then,

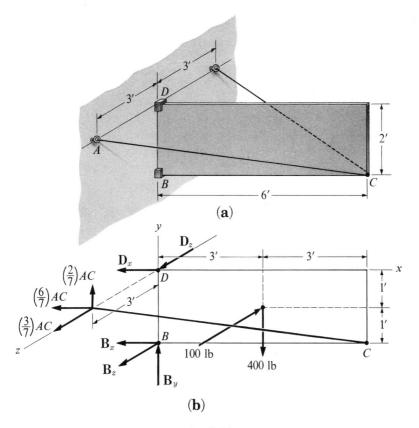

Fig. 3-23

$\Sigma M_{D_z} = 0$

$$2B_x - 400(3) = 0$$

$$\mathbf{B}_x = 600 \text{ lb} \rightarrow$$

$\Sigma M_{D_y} = 0$

$$\left(\frac{6}{7}\right)AC(3) - 100(3) = 0$$

$$\mathbf{AC} = \left(\frac{7}{6}\right)100 = 117 \text{ lb } T$$

$\Sigma M_{D_z} = 0$

$$\left(\frac{2}{7}\right)117(3) + 2B_z - 100(1) = 0$$

$$\mathbf{B}_z = 0$$

By summation of forces in the x, y, and z directions,

$$\Sigma F_x = 0$$

$$D_x - 600 + \left(\frac{6}{7}\right)117 = 0$$

$$\mathbf{D}_x = 500 \text{ lb } \leftarrow$$

$$\Sigma F_y = 0$$

$$B_y + \left(\frac{2}{7}\right)117 - 400 = 0$$

$$\mathbf{B}_y = 367.7 \text{ lb } \uparrow$$

$$\Sigma F_z = 0$$

$$D_z + \left(\frac{3}{7}\right)117 - 100 = 0$$

$$\mathbf{D}_z = 50.0 \text{ lb } \swarrow$$

PROBLEMS

3-80. The solid homogeneous body in Fig. P 3–80 weighs 1200 lb. It is supported in a horizontal position by a vertical cord at E, a horizontal cord at C, a cord at A in the plane ABC, and a ball and socket at G. Determine the tensions in the cords at A, C, and E.

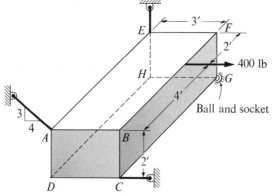

Fig. P 3-80

3-81. The 400-lb homogeneous block is loaded and supported as shown in Fig. P 3–81. Determine the tension in the cable at F.

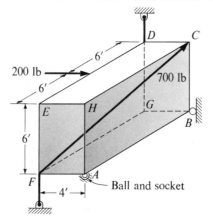

Fig. P 3-81

3-82. The solid homogeneous body shown in Fig. P 3–82 weighs 4000 lb. The face *ABCD* lies in a horizontal plane. Determine all the unknown forces or their components acting on the body.

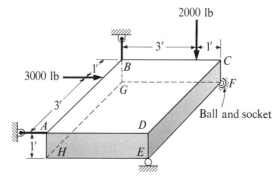

Fig. P 3-82

3-83. The solid homogeneous body shown in Fig. P 3–83 weighs 2000 lb. The face *ABCD* lies in a horizontal plane. Determine all unknown forces or their components acting on the body.

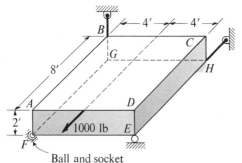

Fig. P 3-83   Ball and socket

3-84. The solid homogeneous block in Fig. P3–84 weighs 2000 lb. Determine the components of the reaction on the block at *H* and all other unknown forces acting on the body.

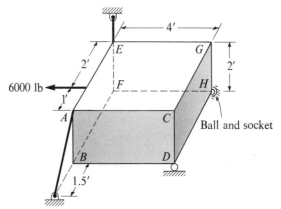

Fig. P 3-84

3-85. A horizontal plate is supported as shown in Fig. P 3–85. The 400-lb force includes the weight of the plate. Determine the components of the reaction at *B* on the plate.

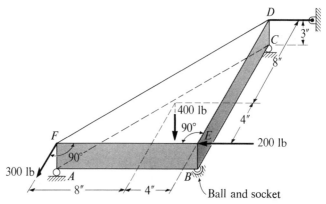

Fig. P 3-85

3-86. In Fig. P 3–86, the two pulleys are fixed on the shaft and the cable at *C* is attached to the pulley. The weight of the shaft and pulley mechanism may be neglected. Determine (a) the tension in the cable at *C*; (b) the components of the force exerted on the shaft by the bearing at *B*.

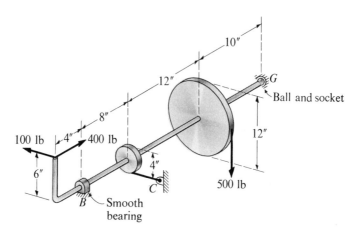

Fig. P 3-86

3-87. In Fig. P 3–87, the pulleys are attached to the shaft. The shaft and pulley mechanism is in equilibrium. Determine (a) the force **P** on the crank; (b) the components of the force exerted on the shaft by the ball and socket at *B*.

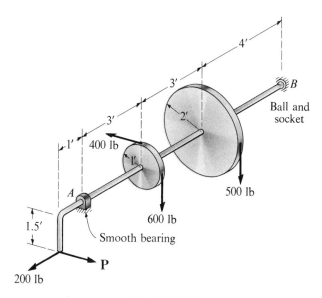

Fig. P 3-87

3-16 SUMMARY

The use of the free-body diagram is given special emphasis in this chapter. This tool is of vital importance in the analysis and solution of these problems.

Also, for the various problems in this chapter, it is essential to recognize the type of force system involved and the number of independent equations available for the solution of each problem. Where a free-body diagram has more unknowns than independent equations, one or more additional free-body diagrams are necessary.

Members of trusses are recognized as two-force members which are either in tension or compression.

Coplanar force systems can be solved by the graphic method using the force and string polygons. As was explained in Sec. 2–6, the graphic method is not well suited to the solution of noncoplanar force systems.

REVIEW PROBLEMS

3-88. The 600-lb body F in Fig. P 3–88 is supported by the four flexible cables A, B, C, and D. Determine the tension in cable C.

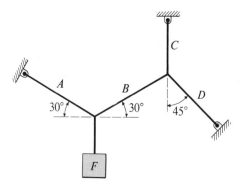

Fig. P 3-88

3-89. The two sprockets on the 1-ton hoist in Fig. P 3–89 have radii of 6 in. and 5.5 in. and are fastened together securely. The chain cannot slip on the sprockets. Determine the pull P on the chain required to lift the 2000-lb load. Neglect friction and the weight of the chain and pulley.

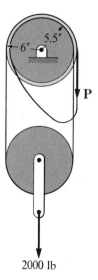

2000 lb

Fig. P 3-89

3-90. The crane shown in Fig. P 3–90 has a weight W of 50,000 lb acting at G. The maximum permissible load on any one of the four wheels (two in front and two in back) is 36,000 lb. Determine (a) the maximum load L that the crane can handle, and (b) the ground reaction on each of the two wheels at B, assuming a load L of 24,000 lb.

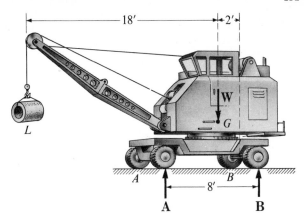

Fig. P 3-90

3-91. A girl weighing 80 lb and a boy weighing 100 lb occupy the seats of a 12-ft-long seesaw, which are located 18 in. from each end. How far from the girl's end of the seesaw would the fulcrum have to be located so that the seesaw would be in equilibrium?

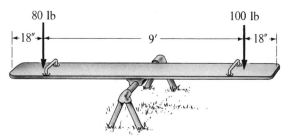

Fig. P 3-91

3-92. In Fig. P 3-92, the 300-lb weight W is attached to the cable which passes over the smooth pulley D and is fastened to member BC. Determine the horizontal and vertical components of the pin reaction at B on member BC.

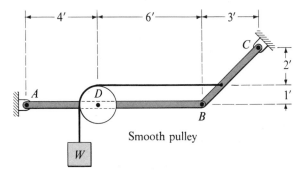

Fig. P 3-92

3-93.   The 500-lb load F in Fig. P 3–93 is supported by the horizontal pin-connected member AC. Determine the components of the pin reaction at B on member BD.

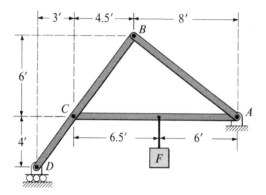

Fig. P 3-93

3-94.   A boy weighing 50 lb steps up on the end of a gate which weighs 200 lb and has its center of gravity at point G as shown in Fig. P 3-94. If the lower hinge carries all the vertical load, determine the reactions at the two hinges on the gate.

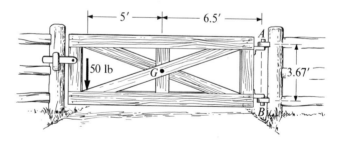

Fig. P 3-94

3-95.   A collapsible TV table is set up, and a man rests his elbow on it, exerting a downward force of 64 lb on the table top as shown in Fig. P 3-95. Determine the horizontal and vertical components of the reaction at the stop B on member AB.

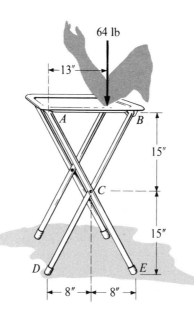

Fig. P 3-95

3-96. Determine the stresses in members AC, DE, and EF of the pin-connected truss shown in Fig. P 3–96.

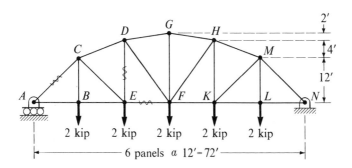

Fig. P 3-96

3-97. Determine the stresses in members BD, DC, and CE of the pin-connected truss in Fig. P 3–97.

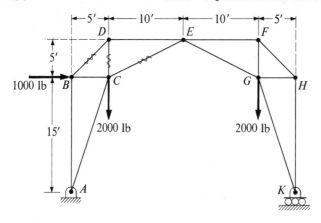

Fig. P 3-97

3-98. Determine the stresses in members *CE* and *BC* of Fig. P 3–98 and the components of the pin reactions at *D* on the pin-connected members *CD* and *DE*.

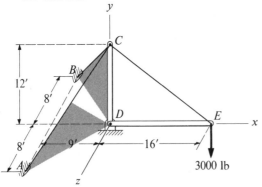

Fig. P 3-98

3-99. Determine the stresses in the cables *AD* and *BD* of the derrick shown in Fig. P 3–99 due to the 3600-lb load applied at *D*. Member *DC* is in the *xy* plane.

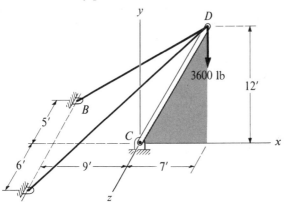

Fig. P 3-99

3-100. The solid homogeneous body in Fig. P 3–100 weighs 1600 lb. Determine the components of the reactions on the block at A, B, and C.

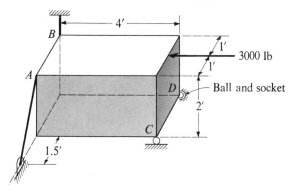

Fig. P 3-100

3-101. The shaft ABE is in equilibrium as shown in Fig. P 3–101. Pulleys C and D are securely fastened to the shaft. The forces acting on pulley D and the cable attached to pulley C at F are in the planes of the pulleys. Determine the components of the reactions at E and B on the shaft. Neglect the weight of the mechanism.

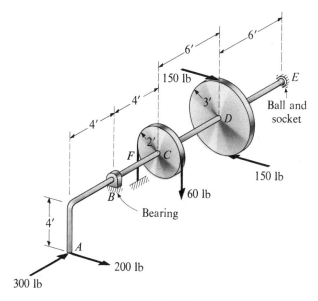

Fig. P 3-101

4 ————————

Friction

4-1 INTRODUCTION

When one body slides or tends to slide on another body, the resisting force tangent to the contacting surfaces is defined as frictional resistance, or simply as friction.

Friction plays an important role in all facets of life. Since it always opposes the motion of one surface with respect to another, it tends to reduce the relative motion of surfaces in contact and may prevent motion altogether. In some cases this is very desirable, and in others it is a constant cause of wasted energy. For example, a great deal of frictional resistance needs to be overcome in machines by the use of lubricants, which however do not eliminate it entirely. On the other hand, in machines such as moving vehicles, drag lines, and hoists, friction is necessary for their operation in the form of brakes, friction drives, etc. When the surfaces in contact are at rest with respect to each other, this resistance is called *static friction*; when they are in motion with respect to each other, *kinetic friction*.

If the friction is static, the amount of friction developed may vary from zero to the maximum friction, called the *limiting friction*. When the limiting friction is exceeded, motion occurs. The magnitude of the limiting friction depends on the normal pressure exerted by the contacting surfaces and on their roughness. The kinetic frictional force is somewhat less than the maximum static frictional force for any given pair of surfaces with the same normal force.

The static friction and the normal pressure are determined by the conditions of equilibrium for all the forces acting on a body. For example, the body shown in Fig. 4–1 has impending motion up the plane under the influence of the applied force **P** and other forces acting on the body. By applying the equations of equilibrium

$$\Sigma F_x = 0: \qquad F' - P \cos \theta + W \sin \alpha = 0$$
$$\Sigma F_y = 0: \qquad N - W \cos \alpha + P \sin \theta = 0$$

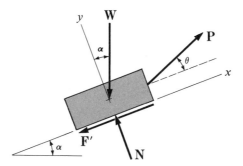

Fig. 4-1

4-2 COEFFICIENT OF FRICTION

The static frictional force may vary from zero to the maximum or limiting friction, which occurs when motion impends. *The coefficient of friction μ is defined as the ratio of the magnitude of the maximum static frictional force* **F'** *to the magnitude of the normal force* **N** *between two surfaces,* or

$$\mu = \frac{F'}{N}$$

Thus, the maximum frictional force which any two surfaces can develop is equal to μN. The value of μ is constant for any two materials for a definite condition of roughness of the surfaces of contact.

If two surfaces move relative to each other, the ratio of the friction developed to the corresponding normal force is defined as the *coefficient of kinetic friction*. The kinetic friction varies somewhat with velocity and generally is somewhat less than the maximum static friction. Since the application of principles and methods of solution rather than answers are of primary importance, the values given in problems in this text are to be used for either static or dynamic friction as required unless both values are specified for a problem.

The value of μ may be determined experimentally as follows: A body is placed on an incline as shown in Fig. 4–2. The angle of inclination θ is then increased until the body starts to slide. The tangent of the angle θ,

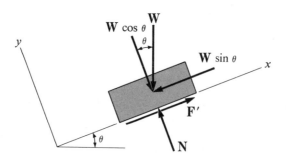

Fig. 4-2

when sliding impends, is the desired coefficient of static friction. The angle of inclination θ, when motion impends, is called the angle of repose. Proof of this is as follows: The weight **W** of the block in Fig. 4–2 is resolved into two components, **W** cos θ and **W** sin θ, as shown. Therefore the equations of equilibrium are

$$\Sigma \mathbf{F}_x = 0: \qquad F' = W \sin \theta$$

$$\Sigma \mathbf{F}_y = 0: \qquad N = W \cos \theta$$

$$\mu = \frac{F'}{N} = \frac{W \sin \theta}{W \cos \theta} = \tan \theta$$

4-3 LAWS OF FRICTION

For more than a century, engineers and scientists have carried on experiments on friction of dry surfaces, which have led to the following general conclusions, known as the laws of friction.

1. The maximum frictional force that can be developed between two surfaces is proportional to the normal pressure.
2. The frictional force which is developed is independent of the size of the contact area, providing no indentation develops in the contact area.
3. The coefficient of static friction increases somewhat for very low pressures and for pressures high enough to produce indentation.
4. The coefficient of kinetic friction increases and appears to become equal to the coefficient of static friction for extremely low velocities.
5. The coefficient of friction is not appreciably changed by small changes in temperature.

4-4   FRICTION PROBLEMS

When analyzing problems involving frictional forces, three possible situations may arise:

1. A situation where impending motion is not necessarily a condition of the problem.
2. A situation where impending motion is specified at all contact surfaces where frictional forces occur.
3. A situation where impending motion is specified but neither the type of impending motion (tipping or sliding) nor the particular surface or surfaces where motion impends is specified.

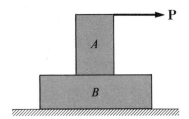

Fig. 4-3

An example of the third situation is indicated in Fig. 4–3. Motion of block A impends to the right. Under the action of the force **P** it may either tip or slide on block B. If it neither tips nor slides on block B, it may move to the right with block B. These possibilities must be investigated before the correct solution can be determined.

Example 4-1   The box A in Fig. 4–4a weighs 500 lb. The coefficient of friction between the box and the plane is 0.50. Determine the frictional force acting on the body.

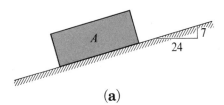

Fig. 4-4   **(a)**

Solution: A free-body diagram of the box is shown in Fig. 4–4b. Assume that the body is in equilibrium. Also, since motion is not known to impend, the frictional force will be assumed to be somewhat less than μN and will be designated as F rather than F'. For this type of problem, where F is assumed, a final check must be made to determine if the value of F is

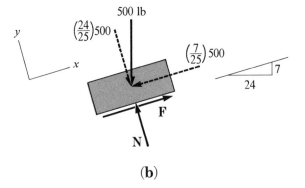

(b)

Fig. 4-4

greater or less than F'. If F is found to be greater than F', the limiting friction F' will be the magnitude of the frictional force acting on the body.
The components of the 500-lb force are shown by dashed vectors. The
equations of equilibrium give the following results:

$\Sigma F_y = 0$

$$N - \left(\frac{24}{25}\right)500 = 0$$

$$N = 480 \text{ lb}$$

$\Sigma F_x = 0$

$$F - \left(\frac{7}{25}\right)500 = 0$$

$$F = 140 \text{ lb}$$

Check: $F' = \mu N = 0.5(480) = 240 \text{ lb};$ $240 > 140$

Therefore, motion is not impending and the frictional force developed
is 140 lb.

Example 4-2   The symmetrical cylinder in Fig. 4–5a weighs 600 lb. The vertical
wall is smooth and the coefficient of friction between the cylinder and the
horizontal plane is 0.20. Determine the greatest value **P** can have without
causing the cylinder to turn.

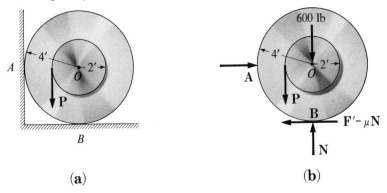

(a)   (b)

Fig. 4-5

Solution: A free-body diagram of the cylinder is shown in Fig. 4–5b. Since motion is impending, the magnitude of the frictional force at B will be μN. The equations of equilibrium and friction give the following results:

$$\Sigma F_y = 0$$

$$N - P - 600 = 0$$
$$N = 600 + P$$

$$\Sigma M_O = 0$$

$$0.2N(4) - 2P = 0$$
$$2P = 0.8N$$
$$2P = 0.8(600 + P) = 480 + 0.8P$$
$$1.2P = 480$$
$$P = 400 \text{ lb } \downarrow$$

Example 4-3   A rectangular block of wood, as shown in Fig. 4–6a, weighs 480 lb, and the coefficient of friction between the block and the floor is 0.20. If the force **P** is gradually increased until motion ensues, will the block slide or will it tip?

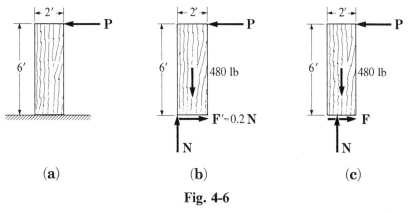

Fig. 4-6

Solution: The problem states that motion ensues, but it is not known whether the block slides along the plane or whether it tips about the lower left corner.

If the body tips before it slides, the normal force **N** will act at the lower left corner of the block, as shown in Fig. 4–6b, and the magnitude of the frictional force **F** will be less than the magnitude of the limiting friction **F′**. If the block slides before it tips, the frictional force will equal its limiting value F' and the normal force **N** will act somewhat to the right of the lower left corner, as shown in Fig. 4–6c.

In this example two values of **P** will be determined, one required to tip the block without sliding and one required to slide the block without tipping it. The smaller value of **P** is the correct result.

The free-body diagram of the block on the verge of tipping is shown in Fig. 4–6b. Taking moments with respect to the lower left-hand corner O,

$\Sigma M_O = 0$

$$6P - 480(1) = 0$$
$$\mathbf{P} = 80 \text{ lb} \leftarrow \text{to tip}$$

Fig. 4–6c shows a free-body diagram of the block with sliding motion impending. By summation of forces in the x and y directions,

$\Sigma F_y = 0$

$$N - 480 = 0$$
$$\mathbf{N} = 480 \text{ lb} \uparrow$$

$\Sigma F_x = 0$

$$P - \mu N = 0$$
$$P - 0.2(480) = 0$$
$$\mathbf{P} = 96 \text{ lb} \leftarrow \text{to slide}$$

Since it requires a load of 96 lb to slide the block, the block will tip when the magnitude of force $\mathbf{P}$ reaches 80 lb.

Example 4-4   The homogeneous cylinder A in Fig. 4–7a weighs 500 lb, body B weighs 300 lb, and body C weighs 200 lb. The coefficients of friction are 0.40 between body A and the plane, and 0.20 between body B and the plane. All other surfaces of contact are smooth. Determine the magnitude of couple $\mathbf{T}$ that will cause body A to have impending motion clockwise.

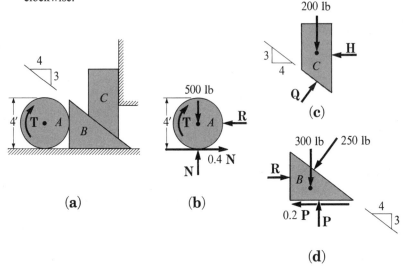

Fig. 4-7

Solution: Assume sliding impends between body A and the plane: Fig. 4–7b is a free-body diagram of body A. There are three unknowns and three independent equations of equilibrium. Therefore by summation of forces,

$\Sigma \mathbf{F}_y = 0$

$$N - 500 = 0$$
$$\mathbf{N} = 500 \text{ lb} \uparrow$$

$\Sigma \mathbf{F}_x = 0$

$$\mathbf{R} = 0.4N = 0.4(500) = 200 \text{ lb} \leftarrow$$

Now assume body A does not slide but rolls without sliding so that bodies B and C will impend to the right and upward respectively: Figs. 4–7c and 4–7d are free-body diagrams of bodies C and B respectively. From the free-body diagram in Fig. 4–7c,

$\Sigma \mathbf{F}_y = 0$

$$\left(\frac{4}{5}\right)Q - 200 = 0$$
$$\mathbf{Q} = \left(\frac{5}{4}\right)200 = 250 \text{ lb}$$

From the free-body diagram in Fig. 4–7d,

$\Sigma \mathbf{F}_y = 0$

$$P - \left(\frac{4}{5}\right)250 - 300 = 0$$
$$\mathbf{P} = 500 \text{ lb} \uparrow$$
$$0.2P = 100 \text{ lb}$$

$\Sigma \mathbf{F}_x = 0$

$$R - 100 - \left(\frac{3}{5}\right)250 = 0$$
$$\mathbf{R} = 250 \text{ lb} \rightarrow$$

Since the maximum force R that body A can exert against body B is 200 lb, sliding of body A will impend. Therefore, by the summation of moments with respect to the center of the cylinder,

$$T - 200(2) = 0$$
$$\mathbf{T} = 400 \text{ ft-lb} \searrow$$

PROBLEMS

4-1. The body A shown in Fig. P 4–1 weighs 300 lb. The coefficient of friction between the body and the plane is 0.40. Determine the frictional force acting on the body.

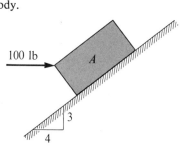

100 lb

Fig. P 4-1

4-2. The 65-lb block shown in Fig. P 4-2 rests on a plane inclined upward to the right at a slope of 5 vertical to 12 horizontal. The coefficient of friction between the block and the plane is 0.30. Determine the minimum horizontal force necessary to cause motion of the block to impend **(a)** up the plane, and **(b)** down the plane.

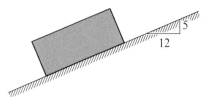

Fig. P 4-2

4-3. In Fig. P 4–3, body *A* weighs 100 lb. The normal force acting on *A* is 120 lb. Determine the magnitude of the force **P** and the frictional force acting on the body. The coefficient of friction between the body and the plane is 0.25.

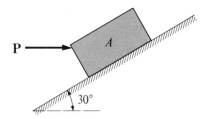

Fig. P 4-3

4-4. Block *A* in Fig. P 4–4 weighs 50 lb and block *B* weighs 80 lb. The coefficient of friction for all surfaces of contact is 0.20. Determine the magnitude of force **P** acting to the right as shown which will cause impending motion of block *B*.

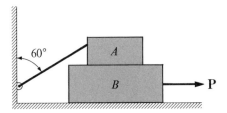

Fig. P 4-4

4-5. In Fig. P 4–5, body *A* weighs 800 lb and body *B* weighs 1000 lb. The coefficient of friction for all surfaces of contact is 0.30. Determine the value of the force **P** which will cause motion of body *A* to impend to the right.

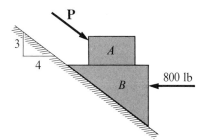

Fig. P 4-5

4-6. The blocks shown in Fig. P 4–6 are separated by a strut, the weight of which may be neglected. The coefficient of friction between the horizontal plane and the 500-lb body is 0.20. The 60° plane is smooth. Determine the magnitude of force **P** necessary to cause motion of the 500-lb body to impend to the right.

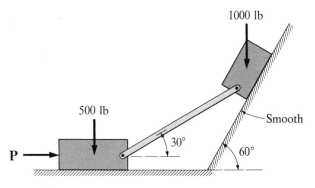

Fig. P 4-6

4-7. The symmetrical cylinder in Fig. P 4–7 weighs 600 lb. The vertical wall is smooth and the coefficient of friction between the body and the horizontal plane is 0.40. **(a)** Determine the greatest value the force **P** can have without causing the cylinder to turn. **(b)** If the cylinder is at rest and *P* is 800 lb, determine all the unknown forces that act on the body.

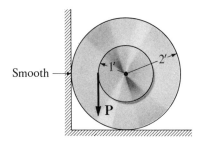

Fig. P 4-7

4-8. In Fig. P 4–8, block *A* weighs 2000 lb and block *B* weighs 1200 lb. The coefficient of friction between block *B* and the horizontal plane is 0.20 and all other contact surfaces are smooth. Determine the frictional force exerted by the horizontal plane on block *B*.

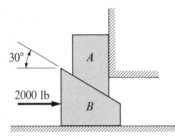

Fig. P 4-8

4-9. Force **P** in Fig. P 4–9 will force wedge *B* to the right, causing block *A* to raise the supporting sill weighing 1300 lb under the corner of a building. Determine the minimum value of force **P** which will cause motion of block *A* to impend upward. The coefficient of friction for all surfaces of contact is 0.20. Neglect the weights of the blocks.

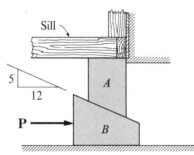

Fig. P 4-9

4-10. In Fig. P 4–10, block *A* weighs 100 lb and block *B* weighs 150 lb. The coefficient of friction is 0.30 between *B* and the plane and 0.20 between *A* and *B*. Determine the minimum value of the horizontal force **P** which will cause block *A* to move to the left.

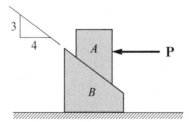

Fig. P 4-10

4-11. In Fig. P 4–11, the 120-lb block is acted upon by the 60-lb force and the unknown force **P** as shown. The normal force of the plane on the block is 180 lb, and the coefficient of friction between the plane and the block is 0.20. Determine **(a)** the frictional force; **(b)** the unknown force **P**.

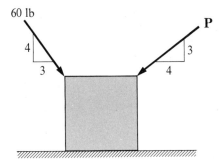

60 lb

P

4

3

3

4

Fig. P 4-11

4-12.   In Fig. P 4–12, the 200-lb cylinder is acted upon by the 50-lb force and the 240 in-lb couple. The radius of the cylinder is 8 in., the vertical wall is smooth, and the coefficient of friction between the body and the horizontal surface is 0.30. Determine all the unknown forces acting on the body.

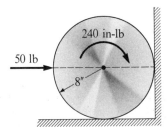

240 in-lb

50 lb

8″

Fig. P 4-12

4-13.   The homogeneous body *AB* shown in Fig. P 4–13 weighs 60 lb. The coefficient of friction at *A* is 0.40. The surface at *B* is smooth. Determine the unknown forces on the body *AB* at *A*.

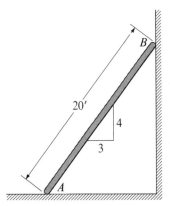

B

20′

4

3

A

Fig. P 4-13

4-14. A 15-ft ladder, on a rough horizontal floor, leans upward toward the right against a smooth vertical wall as shown in Fig. P 4–14. The coefficient of static friction between the ladder and the floor is 0.30. The ladder weighs 60 lb and its center of gravity is located at 2/5 of its length from the base. The base of the ladder is 6 ft from the wall. Determine all forces acting on the ladder when a 180-lb man stands on the ladder so that his resultant weight acts 2 ft from the wall as shown.

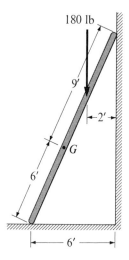

Fig. P 4-14

4-15. A rectangular block of wood, Fig. P 4–15, 10 by 14 by 20 in., stands on end on a rough horizontal floor. The block weighs 50 lb. The coefficient of friction is 0.30. If the magnitude of force **P** is gradually increased until motion ensues, will the block slide or will it tip?

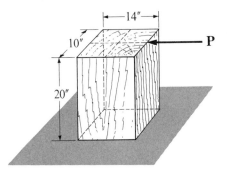

Fig. P 4-15

4-16. The weight of the body in Fig. P 4–16 may be neglected. The coefficient of friction between the body and the plane is 0.40. Determine the tension in the cord and the components of the force exerted on the body by the plane.

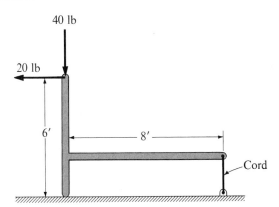

Fig. P 4-16

4-17. In Fig. P 4–17, *A* weighs 150 lb and the weight of *B* may be neglected. The coefficient of static friction for all surfaces is 0.20. Determine the least weight of *C* necessary to prevent motion.

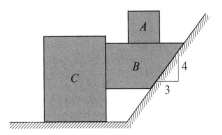

Fig. P 4-17

4-18. In Fig. P 4–18, the uniform bar weighs 100 lb and the block *B* weighs 40 lb. The coefficient of friction for all surfaces of contact is 0.40. Determine the minimum horizontal force which must be applied to *B* to cause it to move (**a**) to the left, and (**b**) to the right.

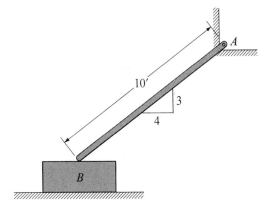

Fig. P 4-18

4-19. In Fig. P 4–19, block A weighs 40 lb and block B weighs 100 lb. The coefficient of friction between B and the plane is 0.25 and between A and B is 0.20. Determine the minimum value of the horizontal force **P** which will cause the block A to move to the left.

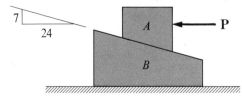

Fig. P 4-19

4-20. Body A of Fig. P 4–20 weighs 1000 lb and the homogeneous cylinder B weighs 440 lb. The coefficients of friction are 0.25 between body A and the plane, 0.25 between A and B, and 0.40 between B and the plane. Determine the magnitude of couple **C** that will cause body B to have impending motion.

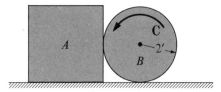

Fig. P 4-20

4-5 BELT FRICTION

The friction that is generated between flat belts and pulleys or drums is used to transmit power or control loads. Fig. 4–8a illustrates power transmission by means of a flat belt. A driving force is transmitted from the driving pulley to the belt because of the frictional resistance developed between the two surfaces. The tension in the belt will vary throughout its length of contact with the pulley (from $\mathbf{T}_S$ to $\mathbf{T}_L$). The free-body diagram of the belt in Fig. 4–8b shows that the belt tension $\mathbf{T}_L$ is greater than $\mathbf{T}_S$ since $\mathbf{T}_L$ must equal not only $\mathbf{T}_S$ but also the frictional force $\mathbf{F}$ developed between the pulley and the belt. When the difference between $\mathbf{T}_L$ and $\mathbf{T}_S$ is such that motion between the belt and the pulley or drum impends,

$$\log T_L - \log T_S = \frac{\mu\beta}{132}$$

where T_L is the larger tension in the belt (lb); T_S is the smaller tension in the belt (lb); μ is the coefficient of friction between belt and pulley or drum; and β is the angle of contact between belt and pulley or drum (degrees).

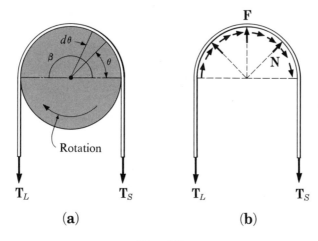

T_L T_S T_L T_S

(a)   (b)

Fig. 4-8

Note: The following discussion involves calculus.

The belt friction equation, given above, may be derived as follows:

A free-body diagram of an element of the belt, subtended by the angle $d\theta$, is shown in Fig. 4–9. The weight of the belt is small and may be neglected in comparison with other forces acting on it. Also the thickness of the belt may be considered negligible in comparison to the radius of the belt, r. Applying the equations of equilibrium to the free-body diagram of the belt in Fig. 4–9, the following results are obtained:

$$\Sigma M_o = 0: \qquad r(T + dT) - rT - rdF = 0$$

and this reduces to $dT = dF$. Also,

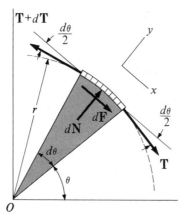

Fig. 4-9

$$\Sigma\mathbf{F}_y = 0: \qquad dN - (T + dT)\sin\frac{d\theta}{2} - T\sin\frac{d\theta}{2} = 0$$

which reduces to

$$dN = 2T\sin\frac{d\theta}{2} + dT\sin\frac{d\theta}{2}$$

The sine of a small angle is approximately equal to the angle in radians. Therefore

$$dN = T\,d\theta + dT\,\frac{d\theta}{2}$$

Since second-order infinitesimals can be neglected,

$$dN = T\,d\theta$$

When motion between the belt and pulley is impending, $dF = \mu\,dN$, and the expression for dT becomes

$$dT = dF = \mu\,dN = \mu T\,d\theta$$

Therefore, $dT/T = \mu\,d\theta$, and as an integral,

$$\int_{T_S}^{T_L}\frac{dT}{T} = \mu\int_0^\beta d\theta$$

where β is the total angle of contact in radians between the belt and pulley. Integrating the above gives

$$\Big[\ln T\Big]_{T_S}^{T_L} = \mu\Big[\theta\Big]_0^\beta \qquad \text{and} \qquad \ln T_L - \ln T_S = \mu\beta$$

The symbol "ln" is the abbreviation for "natural logarithm." The equation above may be written in the form

$$\frac{T_L}{T_S} = e^{\mu\beta}$$

This equation may be changed into the common logarithmic form by multiplying the right side by the log of e to the base 10, as follows:

$$\log_{10}\frac{T_L}{T_S} = \mu\beta(0.4343)$$

In this equation β is in radians. In order to convert the angle of contact to degrees, the right side of the equation is divided by the magnitude of one radian in degrees. Thus,

$$\log\frac{T_L}{T_S} = \frac{\mu\beta(0.4343)}{57.3} = \frac{\mu\theta}{132}$$

where θ is the angle of contact in degrees between the pulley and the belt. This equation may be written also as

$$\log T_L - \log T_S = \frac{\mu\theta}{132}$$

Example 4-5 Determine the maximum weight W that can be slowly lowered by a man who exerts a pull of 150 lb on one end of a rope thrown over a horizontal drum as shown in Fig. 4–10a. Assume the coefficient of friction between the rope and the drum is 0.30.

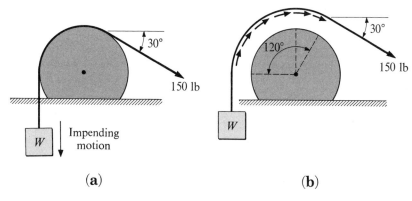

(a)   **(b)**

Fig. 4-10

Solution: Since the rope will pass counterclockwise with respect to the drum, a free-body diagram of the rope in Fig. 4–10 indicates the friction vector acting clockwise or against the motion of the rope. Therefore, $W = F + 150$, which indicates that W is T_L and the 150-lb weight is T_S. The belt friction equation is

$$\log T_L - \log T_S = \frac{\mu\theta}{132}$$

and substituting,

$$\log W - \log 150 = \frac{0.30(120)}{132} = 0.273$$

$$\log W = 0.273 + 2.177 = 2.450$$

$$W = 281 \text{ lb}$$

Example 4-6 The torque $\mathbf{T}$ applied to the pulley in Fig. 4–11 is increased until motion of the pulley impends counterclockwise. If the spring balance attached to the belt at B indicates a tension of 200 lb when motion between the belt and pulley impends, determine the coefficient of friction between the belt and the pulley. The load A is 100 lb.

Solution: The angle of contact is 180°, T_L is 200 lb, and T_S is 100 lb. Substituting all known values into the belt friction equation,

$$\log T_L - \log T_S = \frac{\mu\theta}{132}$$

$$\log 200 - \log 100 = \frac{\mu(180)}{132} = 1.364\mu$$

$$2.302 - 2.000 = 1.364\mu$$

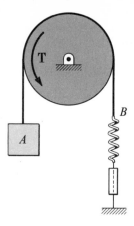

Fig. 4-11

and thus

$$\mu = \frac{0.302}{1.364} = 0.221$$

Example 4-7   Determine the magnitude of force **P** necessary to cause motion
of the drum C in Fig. 4–12 to impend counterclockwise. The coefficient
of friction between body C and the belt AB is 0.40. The force **P** is attached
to a rope which is wrapped securely around the central part of the drum.
Body A weighs 150 lb and body B weighs 45 lb.

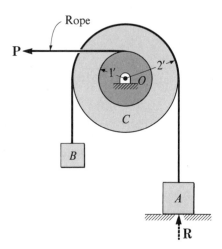

Fig. 4-12

Solution: It is possible for the belt AB to slip on the drum or to roll with the
drum without slipping. If body B were the same weight as body A, the belt
would not slip and this condition would prevail until the weight of B were

reduced to the point where motion between the belt and the drum would impend, that is, until the weight of B would equal T_S in the belt friction equation. The value of T_S for impending motion would be computed as follows:

$$\log T_L - \log T_S = \frac{\mu\theta}{132}$$

$$\log T_S = \log 150 - \frac{0.4(180)}{132}$$

$$\log T_S = 2.177 - 0.546 = 1.631$$

$$T_S = 42.7 \text{ lb} \text{ to ensure impending motion}$$

Since the weight of body B is 45 lb and therefore greater than T_S, the belt will roll with the drum. Thus, by the summation of moments about O,

$$P(1) + 45(2) - 150(2) = 0$$

$$P = 210 \text{ lb}$$

Example 4-8   In Fig. 4–12, let the weight of body B be reduced to 25 lb. The weight of body A remains at 150 lb. Determine the magnitude of force **P** necessary to cause motion of the drum to impend counterclockwise.

Solution: For impending motion determine the tension in the belt at A as follows:

$$\log T_L - \log 25 = \frac{0.4(180)}{132} = 0.546$$

$$\log T_L = 0.546 + 1.399 = 1.945$$

$$T_L = 86.8 \text{ lb}$$

Therefore, the frictional force is $86.8 - 25.0 = 61.8$ lb. By summation of moments about O,

$$P(1) = 61.8(2)$$

$$P = 123.6 \text{ lb}$$

In this case the reaction of the plane on body A is

$$R + 86.8 - 150 = 0$$

$$\mathbf{R} = 63.2 \text{ lb} \uparrow$$

PROBLEMS

4-21.   Body A in Fig. P 4–21 weighs 500 lb and the minimum force P required to raise A is 2000 lb. Determine the coefficient of friction between the belt and the fixed drum B.

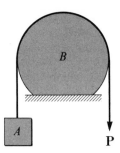

Fig. P 4-21

4-22. The homogeneous block *A* in Fig. P 4–22 is 1 by 1.5 by 3.0 ft and weighs 200 lb. The coefficient of friction between the block and the horizontal plane is 0.40. The coefficient of friction between the flexible belt and the fixed drum is 0.30. Determine the maximum weight block *B* may have without disturbing the equilibrium of the bodies.

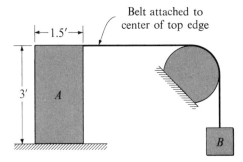

Fig. P 4-22

4-23. Block *B* in Fig. P 4–23 weighs 100 lb. Block *A* rests on a horizontal plane. The coefficient of friction between block *A* and the plane and between the rope and the fixed drum is 0.30. Determine the minimum weight of body *A* if the system is in equilibrium.

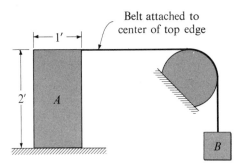

Fig. P 4-23

4-24. In Fig. P 4–24, body *C* weighs 125 lb and body *A* weighs 280 lb. The coefficient of friction between bodies *A* and *B* is 0.40, between body *B* and the plane is 0.30, and between the rope and drum is 0.40. If the 400-lb body *B* has impending motion to the left, determine the magnitude of **P**.

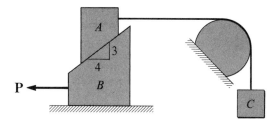

Fig. P 4-24

4-25. In Fig. P 4–25, block *A* weighs 1000 lb, the coefficient of friction between the block and the plane is 0.20, and the coefficient of friction between the cable and fixed drum is 0.30. Determine the minimum weight of *B* which will cause *A* to slide.

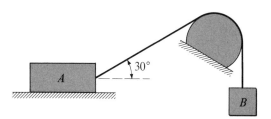

Fig. P 4-25

4-26. Block *B* in Fig. P 4–26 weighs 300 lb and is connected to block *A* by an inextensible belt. The coefficient of friction between *A* and the plane is 0.30, and between the drum and the belt is 0.13. Determine the minimum weight of *A* if the system is to remain in equilibrium.

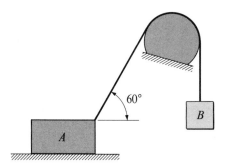

Fig. P 4-26

4-27. In Fig. P 4–27, the coefficient of friction between body *A* and the vertical plane is 0.20, between the rope and the fixed drum is 0.50, and between *W* and the 45° plane is 0.20. Body *A* weighs 50 lb. Determine the least weight of *W* necessary to prevent body *A* from moving downward.

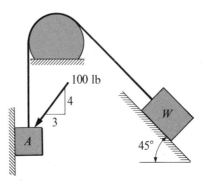

Fig. P 4-27

4-28. In Fig. P 4–28, determine the minimum force *P* necessary to prevent the 100 ft-lb couple from turning the cylinder *A*. The homogeneous bar *BC* weighs 20 lb and the homogeneous cylinder *A* weighs 200 lb. The coefficient of friction between the cable and cylinder is 0.20. The coefficient of friction between bar *BC* and cylinder *A* is 0.40.

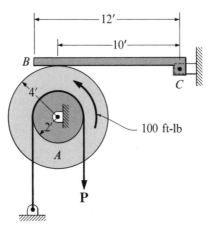

Fig. P 4-28

4-29. In Fig. P 4–29, determine the minimum force *P* which will prevent the 1000 ft-lb twisting moment from rotating cylinder *A* clockwise. The coefficient of friction between the cable and cylinder *A* is 0.50. Cylinder *A* weighs 1000 lb.

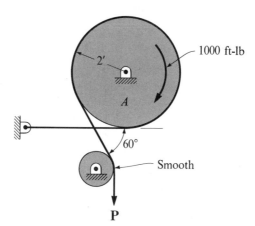

Fig. P 4-29

4-30. The wheel C in Fig. P 4–30 weighs 200 lb and is mounted on a smooth horizontal shaft. Body B weighs 100 lb and is fastened to A by the flexible belt over the pulley. The coefficient of friction between the belt and pulley is 0.25, and between A and the vertical wall is 0.40. Determine the least weight of A necessary to prevent it from moving upward.

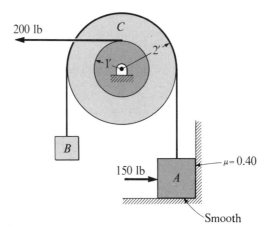

Fig. P 4-30

4-31. In Fig. P 4–31, body D weighs 30 lb, body G weighs 500 lb, and the weight of body ABC may be neglected. The coefficient of friction is 0.50 for both surfaces of contact on body D. The coefficient of friction between the rope and the fixed drum F is 0.30. Determine the magnitude of force **P** such that motion of body D will impend toward the right.

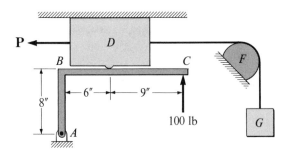

Fig. P 4-31

4-32. A beam, 18 ft long and weighing 400 lb, is supported by a cable passing over a pair of fixed drums as shown in Fig. P 4-32. The coefficient of friction between the cable and drums is 0.20. A man who weighs 150 lb stands at the center of the beam. Determine the distance the man can walk along the beam in either direction without causing the beam to tip.

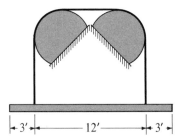

Fig. P 4-32

4-33. A 10,000 lb load W is being held by the brake drum in Fig. P 4–33. Determine the minimum force P which must be exerted by the operator to prevent W from moving downward. The coefficient of friction between the flat belt and the brake drum is 0.60.

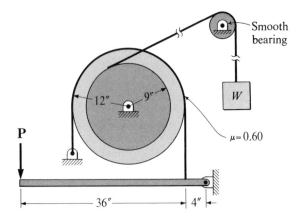

Fig. P 4-33

4-6 S U M M A R Y

Friction is the resistance, stated as a force, developed between two contacting surfaces under pressure, to motion or tendency toward motion of one surface relative to the other. The frictional force always acts parallel to the contacting surfaces and opposes the motion or tendency toward motion.

The limiting friction, F', is the maximum static friction that can be developed between two surfaces before relative motion occurs between the two surfaces. The frictional force, F, may vary from zero to the limiting friction, F'.

The difference between the belt tensions, T_L and T_S, in the belt friction equation is the maximum frictional force that may be developed between a flexible belt and a cylindrical surface. This frictional force occurs when motion between the belt and the cylinder impends or is about to take place.

R E V I E W   P R O B L E M S

4-34. In Fig. P 4–34, block A weighs 100 lb and block B weighs 60 lb. The coefficient of friction between block A and the horizontal plane is 0.20, and between blocks A and B is 0.40. Determine the magnitude of force **P** required to cause block B to have impending motion to the right.

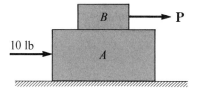

Fig. P 4-34

4-35. The coefficient of friction for all surfaces of contact in Fig. P 4–35 is 0.40. Determine the least force **F** acting on body A that will cause motion of the wedge B to impend to the left. All bodies are considered weightless.

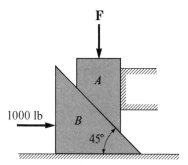

Fig. P 4-35

4-36. In Fig. P 4–36, bodies *A* and *B* each weigh 170 lb. The coefficient of friction between body *B* and the inclined plane is 0.30. Determine the minimum coefficient of friction necessary between body *A* and the inclined plane to keep body *A* from moving down the plane.

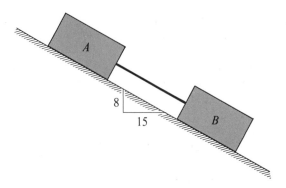

Fig. P 4-36

4-37. The 10-ft ladder in Fig. P 4–37 is placed against a smooth wall. A 200-lb man stands at the center of the ladder. The coefficient of friction between the ladder and the floor is 0.40. Determine the minimum safe angle θ to maintain the ladder in static equilibrium.

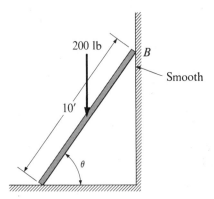

Fig. P 4-37

4-38. In Fig. P 4–38, the rope is wrapped about the central 2-ft drum and the end of the rope is securely fastened to it. The coefficient of friction between the 220-lb wheel *A* and the surfaces of contact is 0.20. Determine the weight *W* that will cause motion of the wheel to impend. The wheel and drum are securely fastened together.

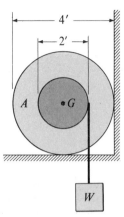

Fig. P 4-38

4-39. A 12-lb body A has impending motion down an inclined plane. When a force of 8 lb, acting parallel to and up the inclined plane is applied to the body, motion of the body impends up the plane. Determine the static maximum frictional force and the slope of the inclined plane.

4-40. In Fig. P 4-40, the member AB weighs 40 lb and its mass center is located at point G. Determine the magnitude of force P necessary to cause the 125-lb block C to impend to the right if the coefficient of friction between block C and the plane is 0.30, and between arm AB and the block is 0.40.

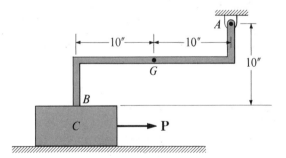

Fig. P 4-40

4-41. A bracket arm, riding on the vertical pipe, is to support a 50-lb load as shown in Fig. P 4-41. Determine the minimum length x of the arm such that the bracket will not slide down if the coefficient of friction between the vertical pipe and the bracket is 0.20.

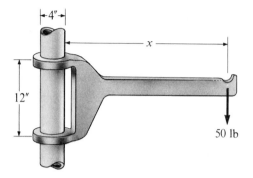

Fig. P 4-41

4-42. A sailor snubs a ship into the dock by wrapping a rope around a post as shown in Fig. P 4–42. The ship exerts a pull of 5000 lb on the rope and the sailor can exert a pull of 125 lb on the other end of the rope. How many 360° turns around the post will be needed to keep the rope from slipping? The coefficient of friction is 0.40.

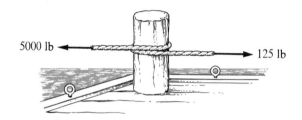

Fig. P 4-42

4-43. Determine the maximum load W the friction drum will hold without slipping if a pressure of 12 lb is applied to the brake arm as shown in Fig. P 4–43. The coefficient of friction between the brake band and the drum is 0.30. The rope supporting the load W is wrapped around and securely fastened to the 12-in. drum.

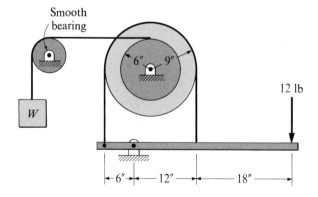

Fig. P 4-43

5 ———

Centroids of Areas

5-1 INTRODUCTION

In the chapter on resultants, the principle of moments often was applied to force systems in order to determine the point of application of the resultant force. In the same way, the principle of moments may be applied to volumes, masses, weights, areas, or lines to determine their respective centroids.

The term "center of gravity" or "center of mass" is often used for the term "centroid." "Center of gravity" or "center of mass" generally refers to masses, while the "centroid" applies primarily to lines, areas, or volumes. In this chapter, centroids of areas only will be considered.

5-2 CENTROIDS

The centroid of an area is a point in the plane of the area so located that the moment of the area with respect to an axis is equal to the algebraic sum of the moments of the distributed parts of the area with respect to the same axis. The axis is usually located in the plane of the area. *The moment of an area with respect to an axis is the product of the area and the perpendicular distance from its centroid to the moment axis.*

In order to understand the concept of the centroid of an area, consider any rectangular area such as shown in Fig. 5–1, which is divided

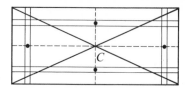

Fig. 5-1

into very narrow strips parallel to the base. The centroid of each narrow strip lies at its midpoint. The locus of these midpoints will lie on a line bisecting the top and bottom sides of the rectangular area. Now divide the area into very narrow vertical strips parallel to the sides. The centroid of each vertical strip lies at its midpoint. The locus of these midpoints will lie on a line bisecting the two sides of the rectangle. The centroid C of the rectangle will lie at the intersection of the two bisecting lines, which is at their midpoints.

In a similar way, the centroid of a triangle may be found as the point of intersection of the median lines, as illustrated in Fig. 5–2. It is apparent that the centroid of a circular area is at the center of the area.

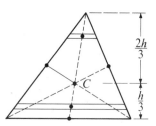

Fig. 5-2

5-3 CENTROIDS OF COMPOSITE AREAS

The centroid of a composite area, which may consist of a number of regular and irregular shapes, is determined by using the principle of moments applied to areas. This may be expressed as follows: *The moment of the composite area is equal to the algebraic sum of the moments of its component parts.*

For regular shapes, the composite area can be separated into rectangles, squares, triangles, or circles. It is desirable to indicate on a sketch the parts into which the composite area is divided. The following example illustrates this procedure.

Example 5-1   Locate the centroid of the shaded composite area shown in Fig. 5–3a with respect to the x and y axes.

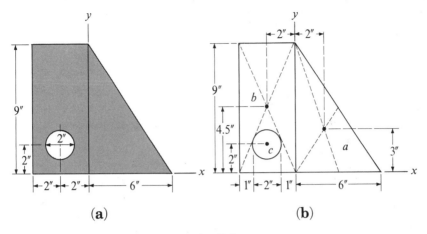

(a)   (b)

Fig. 5-3

Solution: This composite area can be divided into three regular areas: a rectangle, a triangle, and a circle, as shown in Fig. 5–3b. The circle is considered a negative area.

Applying the principle of moments to this composite area,

$$A = a + b + c$$
$$A\bar{x} = ax_1 + bx_2 + cx_3$$

Substituting values,

$$A = 27 + 36 - 3.14 = 59.86$$

and

$$59.86\bar{x} = 27(2) + 36(-2) - 3.14(-2) = -11.72$$

$$\bar{x} = -\frac{11.72}{59.86} = 0.196 \text{ in. to the left of } y \text{ axis}$$

By the same procedure,

$$\bar{y} = 3.95 \text{ in. above } x \text{ axis}$$

All necessary data for each area may be arranged in compact form as indicated in the following table:

Symbol	Area in.^{2}	$\bar{x}$ in.	M_y in.	$\bar{y}$ in.	M_x in.
a	27.00	2	54.00	3.0	81.00
b	36.00	−2	−72.00	4.5	162.00
c	−3.14	−2	6.28	2.0	−6.28
	59.86		−11.72		236.72

$$\bar{x} = \frac{-11.72}{59.86} = -0.196 \text{ in.}$$

$$= 0.196 \text{ in. to left of } y \text{ axis}$$

$$\bar{y} = \frac{236.72}{59.86} = 3.95 \text{ in.}$$

$$= 3.95 \text{ in. above } x \text{ axis}$$

Note: The following discussion, which parallels that above, involves calculus.

For irregular shapes the area may be divided into differential elements. These elements usually can be selected in such a way that only single integration is involved. To ensure a correct solution (1) choose the element so that all parts of it are the same distance from the moment axis, or (2) choose the element so that its centroid can be located with respect to the moment axes.

The following example illustrates the integration method of determining the centroid of an irregular area.

Example 5-2   Locate the centroid of the shaded area shown in Fig. 5–4a with respect to the x and y axes.

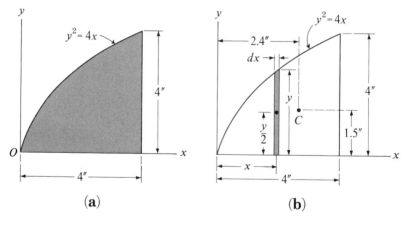

(a)   **(b)**

Fig. 5-4

Solution: On a sketch of the figure, draw the selected element and dimension it completely, as shown in Fig. 5–4b. The expression for the area of the element is

$$dA = y \, dx = 2x^{0.5} \, dx$$

Integrating,

$$A = 2 \int_0^4 x^{0.5} \, dx = 2\left[\frac{2}{3}x^{1.5}\right]_0^4$$

$$A = \frac{32}{3} \text{ sq in.}$$

The expression for the moment of the element with respect to the y axis is

$$dM_y = x \, dA = xy \, dx$$

Integrating,

$$M_y = A\bar{x} = 2 \int_0^4 x^{1.5} \, dx$$

$$A\bar{x} = 2\left[\frac{2}{5}x^{2.5}\right]_0^4 = \frac{128}{5}$$

$$\bar{x} = \frac{128(3)}{160} = 2.4 \text{ in.}$$

The expression for the moment of the element with respect to the x axis is

$$dM_x = \frac{y}{2}(y \, dx) = \frac{y^2}{2}(dx)$$

$$= 2x \, dx, \text{ since } y^2 = 4x$$

Integrating,

$$M_x = A\bar{y} = 2 \int_0^4 x \, dx = \left[x^2\right]_0^4$$

$$= 16$$

and

$$\bar{y} = \frac{16(3)}{32}$$

$$= 1.5 \text{ in.}$$

PROBLEMS

5-1. Determine the location of the centroid of the concrete T-section shown in Fig. P 5–1.

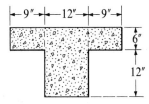

Fig. P 5-1

5-2. Determine the location of the centroid of the cross-section of the built-up wooden beam in Fig. P 5–2

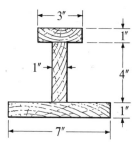

Fig. P 5-2

5-3. Determine the location of the centroid of the cross-section of the angle shown in Fig. P 5–3.

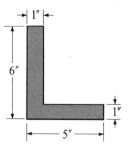

Fig. P 5-3

5-4. Locate the centroid of the shaded area of Fig. P 5–4 with respect to the *x* axis.

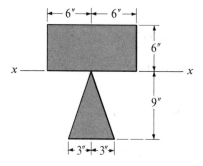

Fig. P 5-4

5-5. For the shaded area shown in Fig. P 5–5 determine the location of the centroid with respect to the *y* axis.

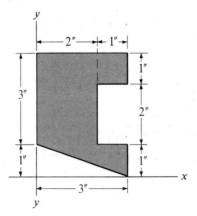

Fig. P 5-5

5-6. Locate the centroid of the area in Fig. P 5–6 and show it on a sketch.

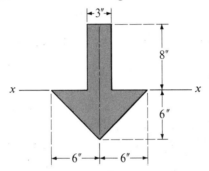

Fig. P 5-6

5-7. Locate the *y* coordinate of the centroid of the shaded area shown in Fig. P 5–7.

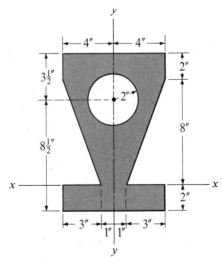

Fig. P 5-7

5-8. Determine the x coordinate of the centroid of the shaded area shown in Fig. P 5–8.

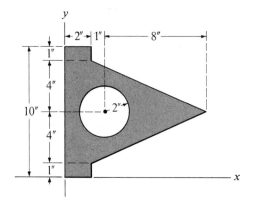

Fig. P 5-8

5-9. For the shaded area shown in Fig. P 5–9 locate the centroid on a sketch.

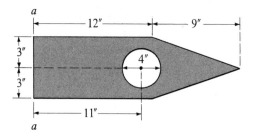

Fig. P 5-9

5-10. Locate the centroid of the built-up section shown in Fig. P 5–10.

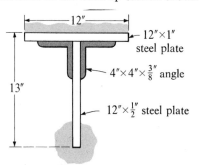

Fig. P 5-10

Note: Properties of a few selected structural shapes are given in Table 3.

Table 3

Properties of Some Structural Shapes

EQUAL LEG ANGLES

Size in.	Thickness in.	Area in.²	I_{x-x} I_{y-y} in.⁴	x & y in.
8 × 8	$\frac{3}{4}$	11.44	69.7	2.28
6 × 6	$\frac{1}{2}$	5.75	19.9	1.68
5 × 5	$\frac{7}{16}$	4.18	10.0	1.41
4 × 4	$\frac{3}{8}$	2.86	4.4	1.14
3 × 3	$\frac{1}{4}$	1.44	1.2	0.84

WF SHAPES

Size in.	Weight lb/ft	Area in.²	Depth in.	I_{x-x} in.⁴	I_{y-y} in.⁴
16 × 7	40	11.77	16.00	515.5	26.5
14 × 8	43	12.65	13.68	429.0	45.1
12 × 8	40	11.77	11.94	310.1	44.1
10 × 8	39	11.48	9.94	209.7	44.9
8 × 8	31	9.12	8.00	109.7	37.0

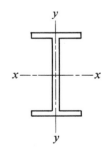

AMERICAN STANDARD BEAMS

Size in.	Weight lb/ft	Area in.²	Depth in.	I_{x-x} in.⁴	I_{y-y} in.⁴
24 × 7	90	26.30	24.00	2230.1	45.5
18 × 6	70	20.46	18.00	917.5	24.5
12 × 5	35	10.20	12.00	227.0	10.0
8 × 4	23	6.71	8.00	64.2	4.4
5 × 3	10	2.87	5.00	12.1	1.2

AMERICAN STANDARD CHANNELS

Size in.	Weight lb/ft	Area in.²	Depth in.	I_{x-x} in.⁴	I_{y-y} in.⁴	x in.
12 × 3	25	7.32	12.00	143.5	4.5	0.68
9 × 2½	15	4.39	9.00	50.7	1.9	0.59
6 × 2	13	3.81	6.00	17.3	1.1	0.52

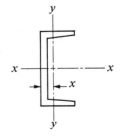

5-11. For the built-up structural section in Fig. P 5–11 determine the *y* coordinate of the centroid.

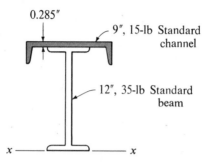

0.285″

9″, 15-lb Standard channel

12″, 35-lb Standard beam

x —— *x*

Fig. P 5-11

5-12. Determine the *y* coordinate of the centroid of the structural section shown in Fig. P 5–12.

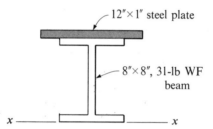

12″×1″ steel plate

8″×8″, 31-lb WF beam

x —— *x*

Fig. P 5-12

5-13. Locate the centroid of the built-up wooden structural section shown in Fig. P 5–13.

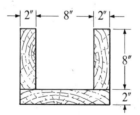

2″ — 8″ — 2″

8″

2″

Fig. P 5-13

5-14. Locate the centroid of the section of the concrete beam shown in Fig. P 5–14.

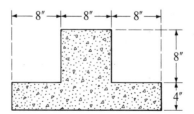

8″ — 8″ — 8″

8″

4″

Fig. P 5-14

5-15. Determine the location of the centroid of the section of the integral concrete floor slab and beam shown in Fig. P 5–15.

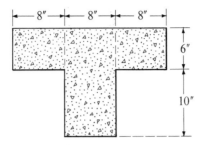

Fig. P 5-15

5-16. Determine the coordinates of the centroid of the area bounded by $y = x^3$, $y = 0$, and $x = 1$ ft, where x and y are in feet.

5-17. Determine the coordinates of the centroid of the shaded area shown in Fig. P 5–17. In the equation $8y = x^3$, x and y are in inches.

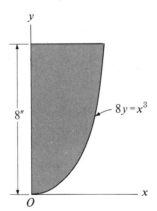

Fig. P 5-17

5-18. Determine the coordinates of the centroid of the area bounded by $y = x^2$, the line $y = 4$ in., and the y axis. In the equation $y = x^2$, x and y are in inches.

5-19. Determine the coordinates of the centroid of the shaded area shown in Fig. P 5–19 and locate it on a sketch.

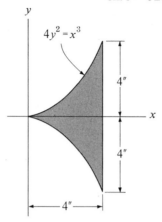

Fig. P 5-19

5-20. Determine the coordinates of the centroid of the area in Fig. P 5–20 bounded by the parabola $x^2 = y$, the line $y - x = 2$, and the y axis.

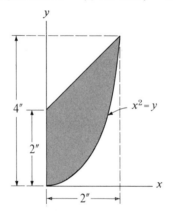

Fig. P 5-20

5-21. Determine the coordinates of the centroid of the shaded area shown in Fig. P 5–21.

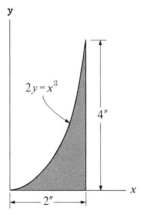

Fig. P 5-21

5-22. Determine the x coordinate of the centroid of the shaded area shown in Fig. P 5–22.

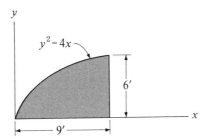

Fig. P 5-22

5-23. Determine the x coordinate of the centroid of the shaded area shown in Fig. P 5–23.

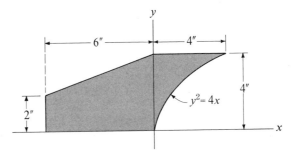

Fig. P 5-23

5-24. For the shaded area shown in Fig. P 5–24 determine the x coordinate of the centroid.

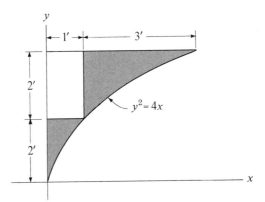

Fig. P 5-24

5-25. For the shaded area shown in Fig. P 5–25 determine the y coordinate of the centroid.

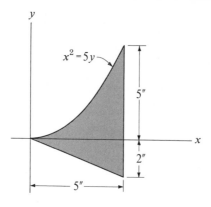

Fig. P 5-25

5-26. For the shaded area shown in Fig. P 5–26 determine the distance from the x axis to the centroid.

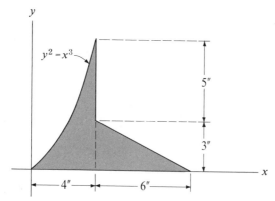

Fig. P 5-26

5-27. Locate the y coordinate of the centroid of the shaded area shown in Fig. P 5–27.

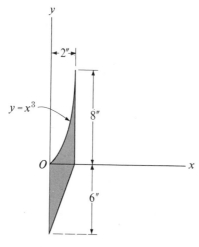

Fig. P 5-27

5-4 THEOREMS OF PAPPUS

A surface area can be generated by revolving a line about an axis in the plane of the line. *The first theorem of Pappus states that the surface area thus generated is the product of the length of the line and the length of the path described by the centroid of the line.* For example, let the arc of length L in Fig. 5–5 be revolved completely about the y axis. The area generated by the arc L is

$$A = L(2\pi\bar{x}) \tag{5-1}$$

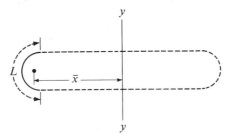

Fig. 5-5

A volume can be generated by revolving an area about an axis in the plane of the area. *The second theorem of Pappus states that the volume thus generated is the product of the area and the length of the path described by the centroid of the area.* For example, let the area in Fig. 5–6 be rotated completely about the y axis. The volume generated by the area is

$$V = A(2\pi\bar{x}) \tag{5-2}$$

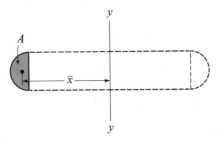

Fig. 5-6

Example 5-3 Determine the surface area of the cone generated by revolving the line in Fig. 5–7 about the y axis.

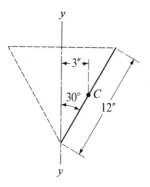

Fig. 5-7

Solution: The x coordinate of the centroid of the line is $\bar{x} = \frac{1}{2}(12) \sin 30°$
= 3 in. Using Eq. 5-1,

$$A = 2\pi(3)12 = 72\pi = 226 \text{ sq in.}$$

Example 5-4 Determine the volume generated by revolving the rectangle in Fig. 5–8 about the x axis.

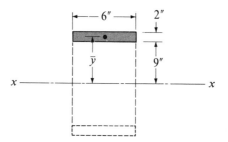

Fig. 5-8

Solution: The y coordinate of the centroid of the area is $\bar{y} = 10$ in. Applying Eq. 5–2,

$$V = 2\pi(10)12 = 240\pi \doteq 753 \text{ cu in.}$$

PROBLEMS

5-28. Determine, by use of the theorems of Pappus, the centroid of a semi-circular area.

5-29. Determine, by use of the theorems of Pappus, the centroid of a semi-circular wire.

5-30. Determine, by use of the theorems of Pappus, the volume of a right circular cone.

5-31. Determine the volume generated if the circle in Fig. P 5–31 is revolved about the y axis. Use the theorems of Pappus.

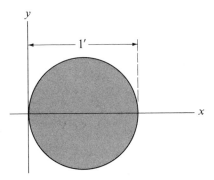

Fig. P 5-31

5-32. The composite area in Fig. P 5–32 is revolved about the y axis to generate a solid of revolution. Determine the volume of the solid.

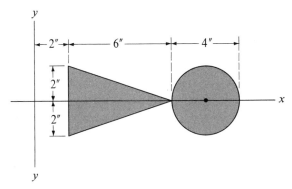

Fig. P 5-32

5-33. Determine the location of the centroid of the shaded area of Fig. P 5–33 with respect to the x axis.

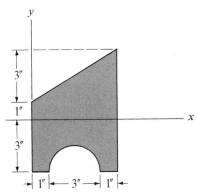

Fig. P 5-33

5-34. For the area shown in Fig. P 5–34 determine the distance from the y axis to the centroid.

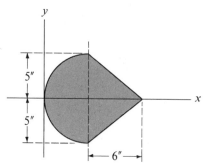

Fig. P 5-34

5-5 CENTER OF PRESSURE

When a force is exerted on a body over a large area, it is called a *distributed force*. The pressure of wind on the side of a building, water on the face of a dam, or grain or granular material on the floor of a bin are examples of distributed loads or forces.

The distributed load or force can be visualized as a number of concentrated forces, each acting over a small area. These forces generally constitute a parallel force system. The resultant force can be obtained by the algebraic addition of these forces and by the application of the principle of moments to a parallel force system. The intersection of the line of action of the resultant of the distributed force system and the plane on which it acts is designated the *center of pressure*.

A distributed force system is represented by a *pressure diagram*. The entire area of the pressure diagram represents the magnitude of the resultant of the distributed force system. The centroid of the pressure diagram represents the point of application of the resultant of the distributed force. If the intensity of the distributed force remains constant, the pressure diagram will be rectangular. If the intensity of the distributed force varies uniformly in one direction, the pressure diagram will be a trapezoid which may be divided into a rectangle and a triangle. However if the intensity of the distributed force varies nonuniformly, the pressure diagram will be irregular in shape. The area and center of pressure of such a pressure diagram will be determined by integration, using calculus.

Proof that the area of the pressure diagram represents the magnitude of the resultant of the distributed force and that the centroid of the pressure diagram locates the point of application of the resultant is as follows:

Let the ordinate q of the pressure diagram shown in Fig. 5–9 indicate the average intensity of the load over one lineal foot of the beam in pounds per lineal foot. The load on an element of area of the beam one foot long is $q(1)$. Let $f = q(1)$. It is apparent that $q(1)$ also represents an element of area, s, of the pressure diagram. Let F equal the total or resultant load. Then $\Sigma f = F = \Sigma q(1) = \Sigma s$. However $\Sigma q(1) = A$, the total area of the pressure diagram. Therefore $F = A$, that is, the magnitude of the resultant force is represented by the total area of the pressure diagram.

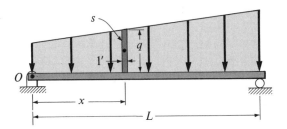

Fig. 5-9

The moment of the component or distributed forces about an axis through point O is

$$\Sigma M_O = \Sigma xf = \Sigma xq(1) = \Sigma xs$$

where x is the moment arm measured from the element of area or force to the moment center O. However the summation of the moments of the distributed forces is equal to the moment of the resultant force, so

$$\Sigma xf = x_p F$$

where x_p is the point of application of the resultant force. By the same principle $\Sigma xs = \bar{x}A$, and since $F = A$ and $\Sigma xf = \Sigma xs$, then $x_p = \bar{x}$. Thus, the center of pressure and the centroid of the pressure diagram are coincident. Therefore the resultant force passes through the centroid of the pressure diagram.

The area and moment of the pressure diagram can be determined by resolving the pressure diagram into simple component parts as indicated in the following example.

Example 5-5   The floor load on a loading dock is distributed as shown in Fig. 5–10a. Determine the resultant load on the beam. Neglect the weight of the beam.

Solution: The distributed load can be divided into four component loads as indicated in Fig. 5–10b. Since the loads are represented by the areas of the pressure diagrams,

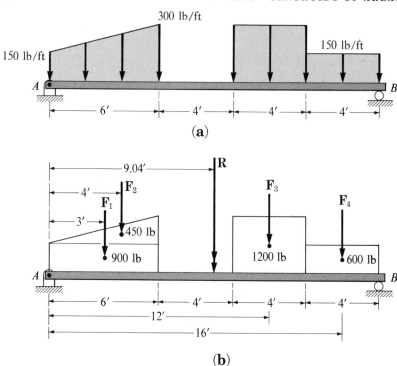

(a)

(b)

Fig. 5-10

$$\mathbf{F}_1 = 150(6) = 900 \text{ lb } \downarrow$$

$$\mathbf{F}_2 = (300 - 150)\frac{6}{2} = 450 \text{ lb } \downarrow$$

$$\mathbf{F}_3 = 300(4) = 1200 \text{ lb } \downarrow$$

$$\mathbf{F}_4 = 150(4) = 600 \text{ lb } \downarrow$$

The resultant load **R** equals

$$\mathbf{F}_1 + \mathbf{F}_2 + \mathbf{F}_3 + \mathbf{F}_4 = 3150 \text{ lb } \downarrow$$

The moment of the resultant load with respect to an axis at A is

$$M_A = 3150\bar{x} = 900(3) + 450(4) + 1200(12) + 600(16)$$

$$3150\bar{x} = 2700 + 1800 + 14{,}400 + 9600 = 28{,}500 \text{ ft-lb } \searrow$$

$$\bar{x} = \frac{28{,}500}{3150} = 9.04 \text{ ft to right of left end}$$

Note: The following discussion, which parallels that above, involves calculus.

Let the ordinate q of the pressure diagram shown in Fig. 5–11 indicate the intensity of the load at any point on the beam in pounds

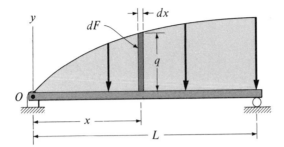

Fig. 5-11

per lineal foot. The load dF on an element of area of the beam of length dx, assuming variation of the load in only one direction, is $dF = q\,dx$, and the total load is

$$F = \int_0^L q\,dx = A$$

the area of the pressure diagram. Thus the area of the pressure diagram represents the total distributed load.

The moment of all the component forces about an axis through point O is

$$\Sigma M_0 = \int_0^L x\,dF = \int_0^L xq\,dx = \bar{x}A = x_p F$$

where x is the moment arm measured from the element of area or force to the moment center O, and x_p is the point of application of the resultant force. Since $F = A$, $\bar{x} = x_p$ and the centroid of the pressure area is coincident with the center of pressure or point of application of the resultant force. Therefore the moment of the resultant force about an axis through O is the same as the moment of the area of the pressure diagram with respect to point O. The following example illustrates this procedure.

Example 5-6   The beam in Fig. 5–12 is subjected to a pressure that varies as indicated. The pressure $q = x^2$ is in pounds per linear foot and the distance x, in feet, is measured from the left support. Determine the resultant of the pressure acting on the beam. Neglect the weight of the beam.

Solution: The force dF at a distance x from the left support is equal to the product of the load intensity (pounds per foot) and the length dx (feet):

$$dF = q\,dx = x^2\,dx$$

The resultant force on the beam is

$$\mathbf{F} = \int_0^{20} x^2\,dx = \left[\frac{x^3}{3}\right]_0^{20} = 2667\ \text{lb} \downarrow$$

The moment of the force $\mathbf{dF}$ with respect to an axis at A perpendicular to the plane of the paper is

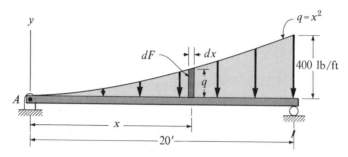

Fig. 5-12

$$dM_A = x \, dF = x^3 \, dx$$

and the resultant moment is

$$M_A = \int_0^{20} x^3 \, dx = \left[\frac{x^4}{4}\right]_0^{20}$$

$$= \frac{160,000}{4} = 40,000 \text{ ft-lb} \searrow$$

The distance from A to the resultant force is

$$\bar{x} = \frac{40,000}{2667} = 15 \text{ ft to right of } A$$

PROBLEMS

5-35. Determine the resultant of the force system shown in Fig. P 5–35.

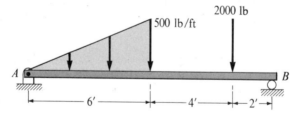

Fig. P 5-35

5-36. Determine the resultant of the distributed force system shown in Fig. P 5–36.

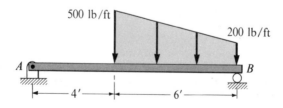

Fig. P 5-36

5-37. Determine the resultant of the distributed force system shown in Fig. P 5–37.

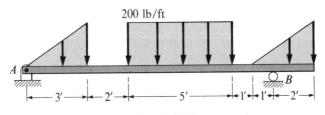

200 lb/ft

A

B

|← 3′ →|← 2′ →|← 5′ →|←1′→|←1′→|← 2′ →|

Fig. P 5-37

5-38. Determine the reactions on the beam shown in Fig. P 5–38.

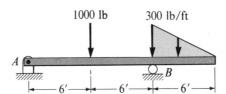

1000 lb   300 lb/ft

A

B

Fig. P 5-38

|← 6′ →|← 6′ →|← 6′ →|

5-39. Determine the reactions on the beam shown in Fig. P 5–39.

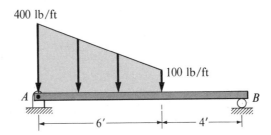

400 lb/ft

100 lb/ft

A   B

Fig. P 5-39

|← 6′ →|← 4′ →|

5-40. In Fig. P 5–40, determine the reactions on the beam at *A* and *B*. Neglect the weight of the member.

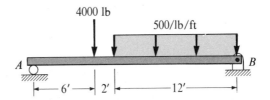

4000 lb

500/lb/ft

A   B

Fig. P 5-40

|← 6′ →| 2′ |← 12′ →|

5-41. Determine the reactions on the beam shown in Fig. P 5–41.

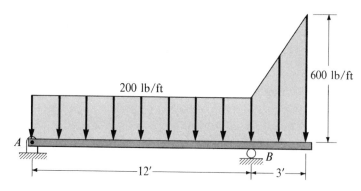

Fig. P 5-41

5-42. Determine the resultant of the distributed force system shown in Fig. P 5–42. The pressure, $y = 2x^2$, is in pounds per linear foot, and the distance x, in feet, is measured from the left support.

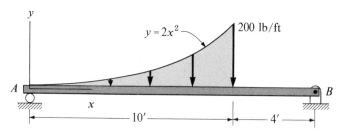

Fig. P 5-42

5-43. Determine the reactions at A and B on the beam shown in Fig. P 5–43 due to the distributed load. The pressure, $y = 10x^2$ is in pounds per linear foot, and the distance x, in feet, is measured from the left end.

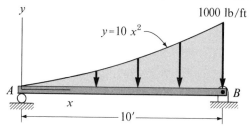

Fig. P 5-43

5-44. Determine the reactions at supports A and B of the beam shown in Fig. P 5–44 due to the distributed load. The pressure, $y^3 = 8000x$ is in pounds per linear foot, and the distance x, in feet, is measured from the right end.

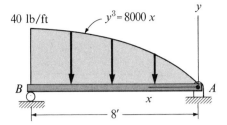

Fig. P 5-44

5-45. Determine the reactions on the beam shown in Fig. P 5–35 at supports *A* and *B*.

5-46. Determine the reactions on the beam shown in Fig. P 5–36 at supports *A* and *B*.

5-47. Determine the reactions on the beam shown in Fig. P 5–37 at supports *A* and *B*.

5-48. Determine the reactions on the beam shown in Fig. P 5–42 at supports *A* and *B*.

6 ───────────

Second Moments of
Areas or Moments
of Inertia

6-1 DEFINITIONS

The second moment of an area, generally called the moment of inertia of the area, is involved in the calculation of certain stresses in beams and columns. *The moment of inertia of an element of an area with respect to a moment axis in the plane of the area is defined as the product of the area of the element and the square of the distance from the axis to the element, provided that all of the element of the area is the same distance from the axis.* Such an element of area necessarily would have an infinitesimal or differential width.

The moment of inertia of the entire area is the summation of the moments of inertia of all the elements which make up the total area.

When the width of the element of area is finite, only the approximate moment of inertia may be obtained, as illustrated in Fig. 6–1. The area shown is divided into six equal elemental areas, a_1 to a_6 inclusive, taken with the long side parallel to the x axis.

The approximate moment of inertia of the whole area is the summation of the moments of inertia of the six elements and may be

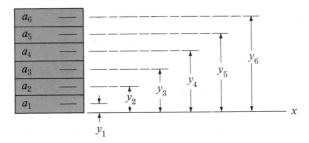

Fig. 6-1

expressed as

$$I_x = \Sigma ay^2 = a_1y_1^2 + \cdots + a_6y_6^2$$

Similarly $I_y = \Sigma ax^2$, where the elemental areas are taken with the long side parallel to the y axis.

As the widths of these elements of area are decreased, the number of the elements would increase and the moment of inertia of the area would become more exact. To obtain the exact moment of inertia, the elements of area must be reduced to infinitesimal or differential widths. The solution for the moment of inertia using such elements requires a knowledge of calculus.

Note: The following discussion involves calculus.

When each element of area has a differential width, dx or dy, as shown in Fig. 6–2a and 6–2b, the exact moment of inertia of the area with respect to the x and y axes may be obtained as follows:

$$I_x = \int y^2 \, da$$

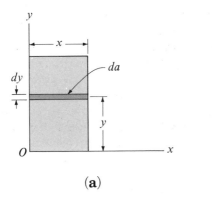 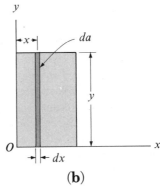

(a)   **(b)**

Fig. 6-2

where $da = x\,dy$, and

$$I_y = \int x^2\,da$$

where $da = y\,dx$.

The element in each instance is chosen so that all parts of the element of the area are the same distance from the moment axis.

Example 6-1   Determine the moment of inertia of the rectangular area shown in Fig. 6–3 with respect to the x axis through the base of the rectangle.

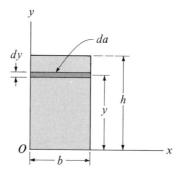

Fig. 6-3

Solution: Draw the element $da = b\,dy$ parallel to the x axis. The moment of inertia of the element of area with respect to the x axis is

$$dI_x = y^2\,dA = y^2 b\,dy$$

Integrating,

$$I_x = b\int_0^h y^2\,dy = b\left[\frac{y^3}{3}\right]_0^h = \frac{bh^3}{3}$$

When the moment axis lies in the plane of the area, the moment of inertia is called the *rectangular moment of inertia of the area*. If the moment axis is perpendicular to the plane of the area, the moment of inertia is called the *polar moment of inertia of area. The polar moment of inertia of an area is equal to the sum of the rectangular moments of inertia with respect to any two perpendicular axes intersecting the polar axis.*

Proof of the above may be shown as follows: In Fig. 6–4 let the area A be of infinitesimal size so that all of area A can be considered to be at the same distance from any axis. The polar moment of inertia of area A with respect to an axis perpendicular to the xy plane at O, the point of intersection of the x and y axes, is $J_0 = r^2 A$. But $r^2 = x^2 + y^2$. Thus,

$$J_0 = x^2 A + y^2 A = I_x + I_y$$

where I_x and I_y are the rectangular moments of inertia with respect to the two coordinate axes intersecting the polar axis.

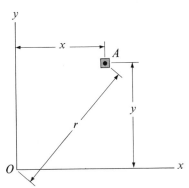

Fig. 6-4

Note: The following discussion, which parallels that above, involves calculus.

An equivalent proof, using calculus, may be given as follows: In Fig. 6-5 the polar moment of inertia, $dJ_0 = r^2\, dA$. However, $r^2 = x^2 + y^2$.

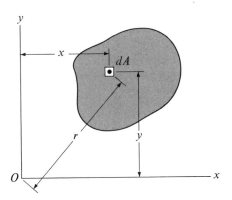

Fig. 6-5

Therefore

$$J_0 = \int x^2\, dA + \int y^2\, dA$$

But

$$\int x^2\, dA + \int y^2\, dA = I_y + I_x = J_0$$

Thus it is shown that the polar moment of inertia of an area is equal to the sum of the rectangular moments of inertia with respect to any two perpendicular axes intersecting the polar axis.

Since the moment of inertia is the product of an area and a distance squared, the unit is in inches or feet to the fourth power. This unit however has no physical significance.

Table 4 shows the moment of inertia of some regular shapes with respect to axes passing through the centroids of those areas.

6-2 PARALLEL-AXIS THEOREM FOR AREAS

It is frequently necessary to determine the moment of inertia of an area with respect to some axis other than the centroidal axis. The parallel-axis theorem provides a convenient relationship between the moment of

Table 4

Moments of Inertia and Radii of Gyration of Simple Areas

GEOMETRIC AREA	MOMENT OF INERTIA	RADIUS OF GYRATION
Rectangle	$I_c = \dfrac{bh^3}{12}$ $I_x = \dfrac{bh^3}{3}$	$k_c = \dfrac{h}{12^{1/2}}$ $k_x = \dfrac{h}{3^{1/2}}$
Triangle	$I_c = \dfrac{bh^3}{36}$ $I_x = \dfrac{bh^3}{12}$	$k_c = \dfrac{h}{18^{1/2}}$ $k_x = \dfrac{h}{6^{1/2}}$
Circle	$I_c = \dfrac{\pi r^4}{4}$	$k_c = \dfrac{r}{2}$
Semicircle	$I_c = 0.1097 r^4$ $I_y = \dfrac{\pi r^4}{8}$	$k_c = 0.2643 r$ $k_y = \dfrac{r}{2}$

inertia of an area and two parallel axes, one of which must pass through
the centroid of the area. *The parallel-axis theorem may be stated as follows:*
The moment of inertia of an area with respect to any axis is equal to the
moment of inertia of the area with respect to a parallel centroidal axis plus
the product of the area and the square of the perpendicular distance between
the two parallel axes.

The parallel-axis theorem may be expressed as

$$I_n = I_c + Ad^2$$

where I_n is the moment of inertia with respect to any axis (in.^{4}); I_c is
the moment of inertia with respect to the parallel centroidal axis (in.^{4});
A is the area (in.^{2}); and d is the perpendicular distance between the
parallel axes (in.).

Note: The following discussion involves calculus.

The parallel-axis theorem may be developed as follows: Referring
to Fig. 6–6, the moment of inertia of the element of area, dA, with
respect to the n axis is

$$dI_n = (d + x)^2 \, dA$$

where d is the distance between the y axis and the parallel n axis.
Expanding and integrating,

$$I_n = \int (d + x)^2 \, dA = d^2 \int dA + 2d \int x \, dA + \int x^2 \, dA$$

$$= Ad^2 + 2d \int x \, dA + I_y \tag{6-1}$$

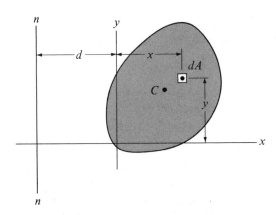

Fig. 6-6 n

The integral of $x \, dA$ is the first moment of the area with respect to
the y axis and is equal to $A\bar{x}$. If the y axis is passed through the centroid

of the area, $\bar{x}$ goes to zero and the expression $\int x \, dA$ becomes zero. Thus Eq. 6–1 reduces to

$$I_n = I_c + Ad^2$$

where I_n, I_c, A, and d are defined as before.

The use of the parallel-axis theorem permits the determination of the moment of inertia of areas by choosing elements other than parallel to the moment axis. Example 6-3 illustrates this procedure.

The equation $I_n = I_c + Ad^2$ shows that the moment of inertia of an area is always least with respect to a centroidal axis.

Example 6-2   Determine the moment of inertia of the shaded rectangular area in Fig. 6–7 with respect to the a axis.

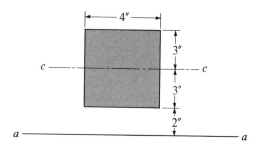

Fig. 6-7

Solution: From Table 4, the moment of inertia of a rectangular area with respect to the centroidal axis is $bh^3/12$. Therefore, using the parallel-axis theorem,

$$I_a = I_c + Ad^2$$
$$= \frac{bh^3}{12} + Ad^2$$
$$= \frac{4(6^3)}{12} + 24(5)^2$$
$$= 72 + 600$$
$$= 672 \text{ in.}^4$$

Note: The following example involves calculus.

Example 6-3   Determine the moment of inertia of the shaded area in Fig. 6–8 with respect to the a axis.

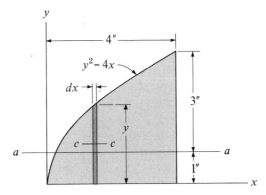

Fig. 6-8

Solution: Select a vertical element $y\,dx$ as shown. The moment of inertia of the element with respect to its horizontal centroidal axis is

$$dI_c = \frac{dx\,y^3}{12}$$

and the moment of inertia of this element with respect to the a axis, using the parallel-axis theorem, is

$$dI_a = dx\,\frac{y^3}{12} + dA\left(\frac{y}{2} - 1\right)^2$$

$$= dx\,\frac{y^3}{12} + y\,dx\left(\frac{y^2}{4} - y + 1\right)$$

Integrating,

$$I_a = \frac{1}{12}\int_0^4 y^3\,dx + \frac{1}{4}\int_0^4 y^3\,dx - \int_0^4 y^2\,dx + \int_0^4 y\,dx$$

$$= \frac{1}{3}\int_0^4 y^3\,dx - \int_0^4 y^2\,dx + \int_0^4 y\,dx$$

$$= \frac{8}{3}\int_0^4 x^{1.5}\,dx - 4\int_0^4 x\,dx + 2\int_0^4 x^{1/2}\,dx$$

$$= \frac{8}{3}\left[x^{2.5}\frac{2}{5}\right]_0^4 - 4\left[\frac{x^2}{2}\right]_0^4 + 2\left[x^{1.5}\frac{2}{3}\right]_0^4$$

$$= \frac{8(64)}{15} - 32 + \frac{32}{3}$$

$$= 12.8 \text{ in.}^4$$

PROBLEMS

6-1.   The area shown in Fig. P 6–1 is symmetrical with respect to the x and y axes. The area is 130 sq in. and the moment of inertia with respect to the a axis is 3420 in.[4]. Determine the moment of inertia with respect to the b axis.

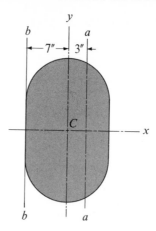

Fig. P 6-1

6-2. The area shown in Fig. P 6–2 is 60 sq in. It has a moment of inertia with respect to the a axis of 900 in.^{4} and a polar moment of inertia with respect to an axis through the centroid G of 1200 in.^{4}. Determine the moment of inertia with respect to the c axis.

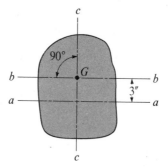

Fig. P 6-2

6-3. The area shown in Fig. P 6–3 is 120 in.^{2} and the moment of inertia of the area with respect to the a axis is 3700 in.^{4}. G is the centroid of the area. Determine the moment of inertia of the area with respect to the b axis.

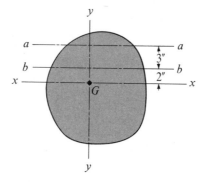

Fig. P 6-3

6-4. Determine the moment of inertia of the shaded area of Fig. P 6–4 with respect to the y axis.

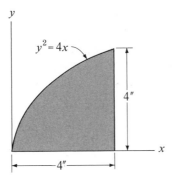

Fig. P 6-4

6-5. Determine the moment of inertia of the shaded area of Fig. P 6–5 with respect to the x axis.

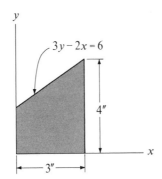

Fig. P 6-5

6-6. Determine the moment of inertia of the shaded area of Fig. P 6–6 with respect to the b axis.

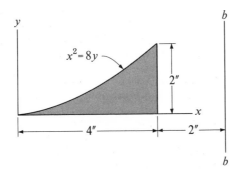

Fig. P 6-6

6-7. Determine by integration the polar moment of inertia of the shaded area shown in Fig. P 6–7 with respect to an axis through its center.

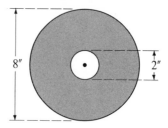

Fig. P 6-7

6-8. Determine the polar moment of inertia of the shaded area in Fig. P 6–8 with respect to an axis through the origin.

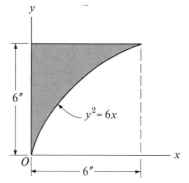

Fig. P 6-8

6-3 MOMENTS OF INERTIA OF COMPOSITE AREAS

In modern structural design, many members used to resist bending or compression have rather complex shapes. These shapes quite often are readily divided into two or more simple component areas. The moment of inertia of the entire composite area can be determined by the summation of the moments of inertia of the component parts with respect to any specified axis in the plane of the composite area. In this calculation the parallel-axis theorem becomes an important and necessary tool.

Example 6-4 Determine the moment of inertia of the shaded area shown in Fig. 6–9 with respect to the y axis.

Solution: Divide the area into a rectangle and a triangle. Since the area of the circle is not shaded, it is a negative area. Also since the y axis does not pass through the centroid of any of the component areas, the parallel-axis theorem will be used. Table 4 gives:

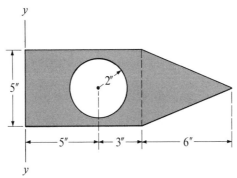

Fig. 6-9

$$I_c \text{ of a rectangle} = \frac{bh^3}{12}$$

$$I_c \text{ of a triangle} = \frac{bh^3}{36}$$

$$I_c \text{ of a circle} = \frac{\pi r^4}{4}$$

For the rectangle,

$$I_y = \frac{5(8^3)}{12} + 40(4^2)$$

$$= 853.3 \text{ in.}^4$$

For the triangle,

$$I_y = \frac{5(6^3)}{36} + 15(10^2)$$

$$= 1530.0 \text{ in.}^4$$

For the circle,

$$I_y = \frac{\pi(2^4)}{4} + \pi 2^2(5^2)$$

$$= 326.6 \text{ in.}^4$$

For the composite area,

$$I_y = 853.3 + 1530.0 - 326.6$$

$$= 2056.7 \text{ in.}^4$$

Note: The following example involves calculus.

Example 6-5   Determine the moment of inertia of the shaded area in Fig. 6–10 with respect to the x axis.

Solution: For the irregular area, let the element be $y \, dx$ taken vertically with its base on the x axis. Using the parallel-axis theorem,

$$dI_x = dx \frac{y^3}{12} + y \, dx \left(\frac{y}{2}\right)^2$$

$$= \frac{y^3 \, dx}{12} + \frac{y^3}{4} \, dx$$

$$= \frac{y^3 \, dx}{3}$$

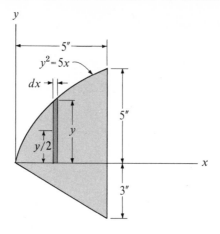

Fig. 6-10

Integrating,

$$I_x = \frac{1}{3} \int_0^5 y^3\, dx = \frac{5^{1.5}}{3} \int_0^5 x^{1.5}\, dx$$

$$= \frac{5^{1.5}}{3} \left[x^{2.5} \frac{2}{5} \right]_0^5$$

$$= 83.3 \text{ in.}^4$$

The moment of inertia of the triangle with respect to the x axis is

$$I_x = \frac{5(3^3)}{36} + 7.5(1^2)$$

$$= 3.75 + 7.5$$

$$= 11.25 \text{ in.}^4$$

And for the composite area,

$$I_x = 83.3 + 11.25$$

$$= 94.55 \text{ in.}^4$$

PROBLEMS

6-9. Determine the moment of inertia of the shaded area in Fig. P 6–9 with respect to the line *A-A*.

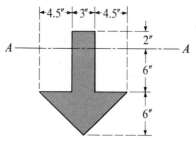

Fig. P 6-9

6-10. For the shaded area shown in Fig. P 6–10 determine the moment of inertia with respect to the *y* axis.

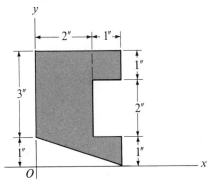

Fig. P 6-10

6-11. Determine the moment of inertia of the shaded area of Fig. P 6–11 with respect to the *x* axis.

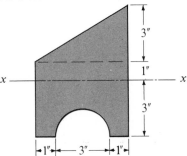

Fig. P 6-11

6-12. Determine the moment of inertia of the shaded area shown in Fig. P 6–12 with respect to the *a* axis.

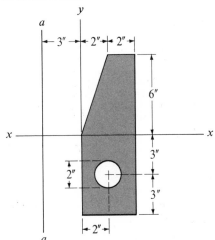

Fig. P 6-12

6-13. Determine the moment of inertia of the shaded T-section shown in Fig. P 6–13 with respect to the centroidal axis *c-c*.

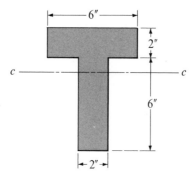

Fig. P 6-13

6-14. Determine the moment of inertia of the shaded area in Fig. P 6–14 with respect to the *x* axis.

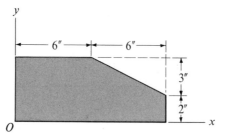

Fig. P 6-14

6-15. Determine the moment of inertia of the shaded area in Fig. P 6–15 with respect to the *x* axis.

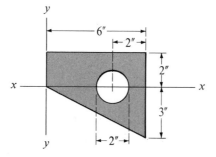

Fig. P 6-15

6-16. Determine the moment of inertia of the shaded area in Fig. P 6–16 with respect to the *x* axis.

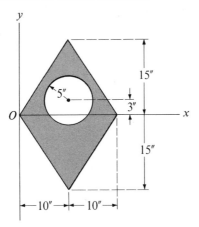

Fig. P 6-16

6-17. Determine the moment of inertia of the shaded area shown in Fig. P 6–17 with respect to the x axis.

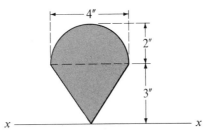

Fig. P 6-17

6-18. In Fig. P 6–18 is shown the cross-sectional area of a beam which is symmetrical with respect to its centroidal x axis. Determine the moment of inertia of this section with respect to the x axis.

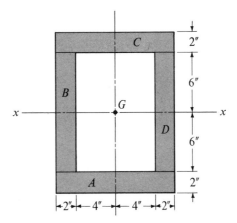

Fig. P 6-18

6-19. For the shaded area shown in Fig. P 6–19 determine the moment of inertia with respect to the y axis.

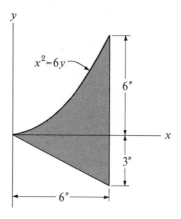

Fig. P 6-19

6-20. For the shaded area of Fig. P 6–20 determine the moment of inertia with respect to the x axis.

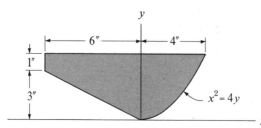

Fig. P 6-20

6-21. For the shaded area shown in Fig. P 6–21 determine the moment of inertia with respect to the x axis.

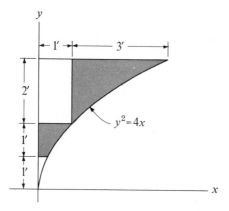

Fig. P 6-21

6-22. For the shaded area shown in Fig. P 6–22 determine the moment of inertia with respect to the x axis.

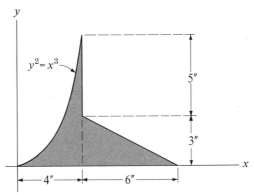

Fig. P 6-22

6-4 RADIUS OF GYRATION OF AREAS

Often it is desirable to express the moment of inertia of an area as a function of the area and a length. *The radius of gyration of an area is that distance from its moment of inertia axis at which the entire area could be considered as being concentrated without changing its moment of inertia.* That is

$$I = Ak^2$$

where k is the distance from the moment of inertia axis to the point at which the entire area could be considered as being concentrated. The radius of gyration k may be expressed as

$$k = \left(\frac{I}{A}\right)^{1/2}$$

The radius of gyration is always greater than the distance from the axis to the centroid. The proof of this statement is drawn from the parallel-axis theorem.

$$I_n = I_c + Ad^2$$

and since $I = Ak^2$,

$$Ak_n^2 = Ak_c^2 + Ad^2$$

Therefore,

$$k_n^2 = k_c^2 + d^2 \qquad \text{or} \qquad k_n = (k_c^2 + d^2)^{1/2}$$

It is apparent that k_n is greater than d.

Usually there is no advantage in associating a radius of gyration with a particular distance in an area. The radius of gyration is used in many problems of mechanics, as in the formula for determining the load-carrying capacity of columns.

Example 6-6 Determine the radius of gyration of the shaded area shown in Fig. 6-11a with respect to the x and y axes.

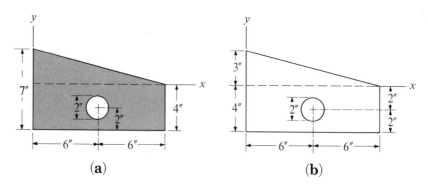

Fig. 6-11

Solution: The trapezoid can be divided into a rectangle and a triangle as shown in Fig. 6–11b. The moment of inertia of a triangle is $bh^3/36$, of a rectangle, $bh^3/12$, and of a circle, $\pi r^4/4$, all with respect to centroidal axes parallel to the base.

Using the parallel-axis theorem,

$$I_x = \frac{bh^3}{36} + Ad^2 + \frac{bh^3}{12} + Ad^2 - \left(\frac{\pi r^4}{4} + Ad^2\right)$$

Therefore,

$$I_x = \frac{12(27)}{36} + 18(1^2) + \frac{12(64)}{12} + 48(-2^2) - \left[\frac{1^4}{4} + (1^2)(-2^2)\right]$$

$$= 9 + 18 + 64 + 192 - (0.79 + 39.48)$$

$$= 242.7 \text{ in.}^4$$

$$\text{Area} = 18 + 48 - 3.14$$

$$= 62.86 \text{ in.}^2$$

$$K_x = \left(\frac{I}{A}\right)^{1/2} = \left(\frac{242.7}{62.86}\right)^{1/2}$$

$$= 3.86^{1/2}$$

$$= 1.965 \text{ in.}$$

$$I_y = \frac{3(1728)}{12} + 18(4^2) + \frac{4(1728)}{12} + 48(6^2) - \left(\frac{\pi 1^4}{4} + \frac{\pi 1^2}{6^2}\right)$$

$$= 144 + 288 + 576 + 1728 - 114$$

$$= 2622 \text{ in.}^4$$

$$K_y = \left(\frac{2622}{62.86}\right)^{1/2}$$

$$= 6.47 \text{ in.}$$

Note: The following example involves calculus.

Example 6-7   Determine the radius of gyration of the shaded area shown in Fig. 6–12a with respect to the x and y axes.

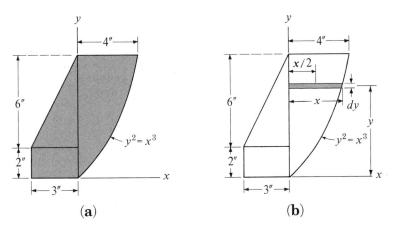

(a)   **(b)**

Fig. 6-12

Solution: For the irregular area let the element be $x\,dy$ taken horizontally with its base on the y axis as shown in Fig. 6–12b. By the parallel-axis theorem,

$$dI_y = \frac{x^3\,dy}{12} + x\,dy\left(\frac{x}{2}\right)^2$$

$$= \frac{x^3\,dy}{12} = \frac{x^3\,dy}{4}$$

$$= \frac{x^3\,dy}{3}$$

Integrating,

$$I_y = \frac{1}{3}\int_0^8 x^3\,dy = \frac{1}{3}\int_0^8 y^2\,dy$$

$$= \frac{1}{9}\left[y^3\right]_0^8 = \frac{512}{9}$$

$$= 56.9 \text{ in.}^4$$

For the triangle,

$$I_y = \frac{6(27)}{36} + 9(1^2)$$

$$= 13.5 \text{ in.}^4$$

For the rectangle,

$$I_y = \frac{2(27)}{12} + 6(2.25)$$

$$= 18 \text{ in.}^4$$

$$\text{Total } I_y = 56.9 + 13.5 + 18.0$$

$$= 88.4 \text{ in.}^4$$

$$\text{Irregular area} = \int_0^8 x \, dy = \int_0^8 y^{2/3} \, dy$$

$$= \left[\frac{3}{5} y^{5/3} \right]_0^8$$

$$= 19.2 \text{ in.}^2$$

$$\text{Total area} = 19.2 + 9 + 6$$

$$= 34.2 \text{ in.}^2$$

$$K_y = \left(\frac{88.4}{34.2} \right)^{1/2}$$

$$= 1.61 \text{ in.}$$

$$dI_x = y^2 x \, dy$$

$$= y^{8/3} \, dy$$

$$I_x = \int_0^8 y^{8/3} \, dy = \left[\frac{3}{11} y^{11/3} \right]_0^8$$

$$= \frac{3}{11}(2048)$$

$$= 558 \text{ in.}^4$$

For the triangle,

$$I_x = \frac{6(27)}{36} + 9(4^2)$$

$$= 148.5 \text{ in.}^4$$

For the rectangle,

$$I_x = \frac{3(8)}{12} + 6(1^2)$$

$$= 8 \text{ in.}^4$$

$$\text{Total } I_x = 558 + 148.5 + 8$$

$$= 714.5 \text{ in.}^4$$

$$K_x = \left(\frac{714.5}{34.2} \right)^{1/2}$$

$$= 4.58 \text{ in.}$$

PROBLEMS

6-23. The two rectangles in Fig. P 6–23 are each 3 by 8 in. (a) Determine the spacing of the areas so that I_x and I_y of the shaded areas are equal.

(b) Determine the radius of gyration of the shaded areas with respect to the *y* axis.

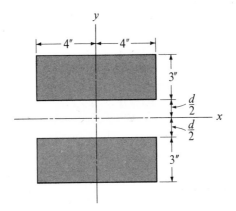

Fig. P 6-23

6-24. Determine the radius of gyration of the shaded area shown in Fig. P 6–24 with respect to the *x* axis.

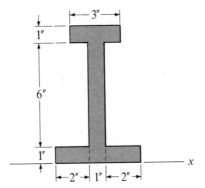

Fig. P 6-24

6-25. Determine the radius of gyration with respect to the bottom edge *a-a* of the channel section shown in Fig. P 6–25.

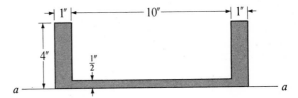

Fig. P 6-25

6-26. Determine the radius of gyration of the angle section shown in Fig. P 6–26 with respect to the centroidal axis *a-a*.

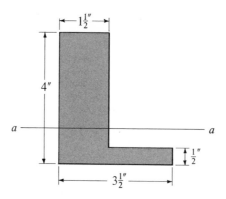

Fig. P 6-26

6-27. Determine the radius of gyration of the shaded area of Fig. P 6–27 with respect to the x axis.

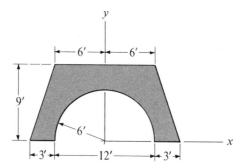

Fig. P 6-27

6-28. Determine the radius of gyration of the shaded area shown in Fig. P 6–28 with respect to the x-axis.

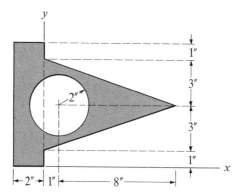

Fig. P 6-28

6-29. Determine the radius of gyration of the shaded area in Fig. P 6–29 with respect to an axis through point A perpendicular to the plane of the area.

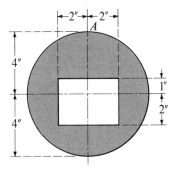

Fig. P 6-29

6-30. Determine the radius of gyration of the shaded area in Fig. P 6–30 with respect to the y axis.

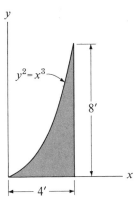

Fig. P 6-30

6-31. Determine the radius of gyration of the column section in Fig. P 6–31 with respect to the y axis. The section is made up of two 25 lb, 12 by 3 in. channels, latticed together as shown.

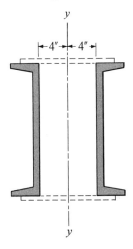

Fig. P 6-31

6-32. Determine the radius of gyration of the column section in Fig. P 6–32 with respect to the x axis. The section is made up of four 3 by 3 by $\frac{1}{4}$ in. angles, latticed together as shown.

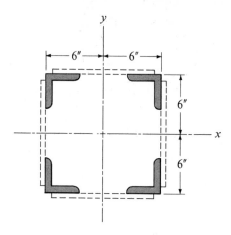

Fig. P 6-32

Answers to
Even-Numbered Problems

CHAPTER 1

1-2. 288 lb →, 84 lb ↓, both through A

1-4. 200 lb →, 224 lb ◿¹₂, both through origin

1-6. (a) 343 lb →, 206 lb ↓, both through A; (b) 274 lb →, 217 lb ³◣₁, both through A

1-8. 200 lb ³◣₄, 179 lb ◿¹₂

1-10. (a) 173 lb →, 100 lb ↑, both through origin; (b) 188 lb →, 68 lb ↑, both through origin

1-12. (a) 9.4 lb →; (b) 52 lb ↑

1-14. 60 lb ←, 20 lb ↓, 30 lb ↗, all through a point on the 70-lb force

1-16. 180 lb ←, 40 lb ↑, 120 lb ↗, all through origin

1-18. (a) 200 in-lb ↻; (b) 120 ft-lb ↘; (c) 1066 ft-lb ↘; (d) 10 in-lb ↻

1-20. 1000 in-lb ↻

1-22. 180 ft-lb ⟂

1-24. (a) 15.05 lb →, 12.15 lb ↓, 5.04 lb ↗; (b) 85.05 in-lb ⟍

1-26. (a) 220 in-lb $\curvearrowright$; (b) 2.20 in.

1-28. 80 lb →, 120 lb ↓, 240 lb ↙, all through origin; 720 ft-lb $\curvearrowleft$

1-30. (a) 75 lb → at A; (b) 50 lb ↑ at B

1-32. 60 lb ↓ at B, 100 lb ← at A

1-34. (a), (b), (c) 240 in-lb $\curvearrowright$

1-36. 30 lb → at A, 110 lb → at B

1-38. 75 lb ↑, 2 ft to right of A

1-40. 40 lb ←, 7.5 ft above D

1-42. 1000 lb $\underset{4}{\diagup}^{3}$, 2400 in-lb $\curvearrowright$

1-44. F, L^4

1-46. L/T

1-48. Yes

1-50. FT^2

CHAPTER 2

2-2. (a) Single force; (b) 75 lb $\underset{3}{\diagup}^{4}$ through point of concurrence

2-4. 102.5 lb $\underset{60}{\diagup}^{83}$ through point of concurrence

2-6. 190 lb $\underset{3}{\diagdown}^{1}$ through point of concurrence

2-8. 2270 lb ← through point of concurrence

2-10. 86.7 lb $\underset{55.9}{\diagup}^{66.1}$ through point of concurrence

2-12. 109.6 lb $\underset{101.4}{\diagup}^{41.4}$ through A

2-14. 146 lb $\underset{111.6}{\overset{93.3}{\diagdown}}$ through point of concurrence

2-16. 437 lb $\underset{14}{\overset{4}{\diagdown}}$ through upper rivet

2-18. 20 lb ↓ at A

2-20. 550 lb ↓, 16.7 ft to right of A

2-22. 67 lb ↑, 0.30 ft to right of **R**

2-24. 30 lb ↓, 15 ft to left of A

2-26. 190 ft-lb $\curvearrowright$ couple

2-28. 104 lb $\underset{94.3}{\overset{43.4}{\diagdown}}$, 1.88 ft upward to right of center

2-30. 350 lb $\underset{4}{\overset{3}{\diagdown}}$, 4.29 in. upward to right of A

2-32. 50 lb $\underset{3}{\diagup}^{4}$, 3.6 in. downward to right of A

2-34. 44.8 lb $\underset{1}{\diagup}^{2}$, 20.6 ft downward to right of O

2-36. 413 lb $176.6\underset{373.2}{\diagdown}$, 0.93 ft downward to left of A

2-38. 10 lb ↑ , 5 ft to right of 50-lb force

2-40. 5000 lb ↓ , 14 ft to right of A

2-42. 30 lb ↓ , 15 ft to left of A

2-44. 36.9 ft-lb

2-46. 34.9 lb from A through -28, 7.83, -19.28

2-48. (a) 150 lb from point of concurrence through 20, 9, -12; (b) 864 ft-lb

2-50. 36.75 lb from ring through 4, -36, 6

2-52. 88.3 lb from origin through -2, 5, 7

2-54. 166.5 lb from origin through 81.4, 123.7, 77.4

2-56. 20 lb ↑ at $x = 0$, $z = 7$ ft

2-58. 10 lb ↓ at $x = -48$ ft, $z = 57$ ft

2-60. 100 lb ↑ at $x = -5$ ft, $z = -3$ ft

2-62. 50 lb ↓ at $x = 1.8$ ft, $z = 1.8$ ft

2-64. 20 lb ↓ at $x = 6.5$ ft, $z = -2$ ft

2-66. 342 in-lb

2-68. 1564 in-lb

2-70. 671 ft-lb

2-72. 5664 in-lb

2-74. 15.32 lb $\underset{5}{\Big\uparrow}^{1}$ through point of concurrence

2-76. 557,500 lb, 8.2 ft $\Big\downarrow^{1}_{6.1}$ downward to left of toe

2-78. $\mathbf{F} = 74$ lb, $\mathbf{R}_1 = 1883$ lb, $\mathbf{R}_2 = 1914$ lb

2-80. 518.7 lb →, 4.65 in. above A

CHAPTER 3

3-10. 2530 lb T (tension)

3-12. $\mathbf{AC} = 500$ lb T, $\mathbf{BC} = 300$ lb C (compression)

3-14. $\mathbf{A} = 1250$ lb $\underset{3}{\diagdown}{}^{4}$, $\mathbf{D} = 850$ lb $\overset{4}{\diagdown}_{7.5}$

3-16. $\mathbf{F} = 2500$ lb ←, $\mathbf{C} = 10{,}310$ lb $\diagup^{4}_{1}$

3-18. $\mathbf{N}$ (normal force) $= 95.2$ lb $\diagup^{4}_{3}$, $\mathbf{T}$ (tensile force) $= 61.9$ lb $\overset{5}{\diagdown}_{12}$

3-20. $\mathbf{N} = 100$ lb $\underset{3}{\diagdown}{}^{4}$, $\mathbf{T} = 20$ lb ↑

3-22. $\mathbf{A} = 125$ lb T, $\mathbf{B} = 248$ lb T, $\mathbf{C} = 200$ lb T, $\mathbf{D} = 173.2$ lb T

3-24. $\mathbf{A}_x = 1000$ lb →, $\mathbf{A}_y = 1133$ lb ↓

3-26. $C = 729$ lb ⟋692 ⟍231

3-28. $C_x = 188$ lb $\rightarrow$, $C_y = 750$ lb $\uparrow$, $E_x = 688$ lb $\leftarrow$, $E_y = 250$ lb $\downarrow$

3-30. $F = 1290$ lb ▭→ 8

3-32. $B_x = 245$ lb $\rightarrow$, $B_y = 625$ lb $\downarrow$

3-34. $C_x = 400$ lb $\leftarrow$, $C_y = 1300$ lb $\uparrow$, $E_x = 800$ lb $\rightarrow$, $E_y = 1600$ lb $\downarrow$

3-36. $A = 1000$ lb $\uparrow$, $E = 900$ lb $\uparrow$

3-38. 167 lb

3-40. $A = 7.51$ kip $\uparrow$, $E = 9.37$ kip ⟋8.61 3.66

3-42. 30 lb, 1.33 ft left of A

3-44. $A = 1000$ lb $\uparrow$, $E = 900$ lb $\uparrow$

3-46. $A = 810$ lb ⟋674 448 , $D = 867$ lb $\uparrow$

3-48. $AB = 1330$ lb C, $DF = 6667$ lb C, $DG = 3330$ lb T

3-50. $BE = 500$ lb C, $CE = 559$ lb T, $FJ = 4000$ lb C

3-52. $CD = 24{,}000$ lb T, $CH = 20{,}000$ lb T, $DH = 16{,}000$ lb C

3-54. $BC = 6900$ lb C, $BI = 3250$ lb T

3-56. $BH = 0$, $AH = 7467$ lb C, $BG = 2915$ lb C

3-58. $BD = 20.32$ kip C, $CD = 0$, $CE = 17.32$ kip T

3-60. $AD = 6667$ lb T, $AC = 0$, $BC = 8330$ lb C

3-62. Partial: $BC = 6900$ lb C, $BI = 3250$ lb T

3-64. Partial: $CF = 0$, $CH = 7350$ lb C, $BC = 7750$ lb T

3-66. $BE = 1600$ lb C, $CE = 2095$ lb C, $AE = 2000$ lb T

3-68. $AC = 530$ lb T, $AD = 572$ lb T

3-70. $A = 3500$ lb T, $B = 1500$ lb T, $C = 3000$ lb T

3-72. $AO = 65.7$ lb T

3-74. $A = 2200$ lb T, $B = 950$ lb T, $C = 1950$ lb $\uparrow$

3-76. $A = 5730$ lb T, $B = 4000$ lb T, $C = 2270$ lb T

3-78. $A = 1100$ lb T, $B = 1600$ lb $\uparrow$, $C = 1000$ lb T

3-80. $A = 1000$ lb T, $C = 667$ lb T, $E = 267$ lb T

3-82. $A = 750$ lb T, $B = 1938$ lb T, $E = 2000$ lb $\uparrow$, $F_x = 2250$ lb $\leftarrow$, $F_y = 2062$ lb $\uparrow$, $F_z = 0$

3-84. $A = 5000$ lb T, $D = 7000$ lb $\uparrow$, $E = 8000$ lb T, $H_x = 6000$ lb $\rightarrow$, $H_y = 9000$ lb $\downarrow$, $H_z = 3000$ lb $\nearrow$

3-86. (a) 1200 lb T; (b) $B_x = 767$ lb $\leftarrow$, $B_y = 86.7$ lb $\uparrow$

3-88. 820 lb

3-90. (a) 23,800 lb; (b) 750 lb $\uparrow$

3-92. 80 lb $\rightarrow$, 120 lb $\downarrow$

3-94. $A = 511$ lb $\rightarrow$, $B = 569$ lb ⟋511 ⟍250

3-96. $AC = 7.07$ kip C, $DE = 1$ kip T, $EF = 6$ kip T

3-98. $CE = 5000$ lb T, $BC = 3780$ lb T, $D_x = 4000$ lb $\rightarrow$, $D_y = 8330$ lb $\uparrow$

3-100. $A = 1250$ lb T, $B = 3300$ lb T, $C = 2550$ lb $\uparrow$

CHAPTER 4

4-2. (a) 53.2 lb →; (b) 6.74 lb →
4-4. 38.6 lb
4-6. 1066 lb
4-8. 640 lb ←
4-10. 75 lb
4-12. $N = 200$ lb ↑, $F = 30$ lb →, $R = 80$ lb ←
4-14. $N = 240$ lb ↑, $F = 62.8$ lb →, $R = 62.8$ lb ←
4-16. $N = 55$ lb ↑, $F = 20$ lb →, $C = 15$ lb T
4-18. (a) 46.8 lb ←; (b) 73.2 lb →
4-20. 400 ft-lb
4-22. 80 lb
4-24. 438 lb
4-26. 540 lb
4-28. 87 lb
4-30. 140 lb
4-32. 6.64 ft from center
4-34. 22 lb
4-36. 0.767
4-38. 188.7 lb
4-40. 55 lb
4-42. 1.47 turns

CHAPTER 5

5-2. 2.29 in. above base on vertical axis of symmetry
5-4. 0.55 in. above x axis
5-6. 0.40 in. above x axis on vertical axis of symmetry
5-8. 3.73 in. right of y axis
5-10. 3.44 in. below top on vertical axis of symmetry
5-12. 6.56 in. above base
5-14. 4.4 in. above base on vertical axis of symmetry
5-16. $\bar{x} = 0.8$ ft, $\bar{y} = 0.286$ ft
5-18. $\bar{x} = 0.75$ in., $\bar{y} = 2.40$ in.
5-20. $\bar{x} = 0.80$ in., $\bar{y} = 1.84$ in.
5.22. 5.40 ft
5.24. 1.62 ft.
5-26. 1.88 in.
5-28. $\dfrac{4r}{3\pi}$
5-30. $\dfrac{\pi r^2 h}{3}$
5-32. 1090 cu in.

5-34. 4.65 in.
5-36. 2100 lb ↓ , 3.43 ft left of B
5-38. A = 350 lb ↑ , B = 1550 lb ↑
5-40. A = 4600 lb ↑ , B = 5400 lb ↑
5-42. 667 lb ↓ , 7.5 ft right of A
5-44. A = 103 lb ↑ , B = 137 lb ↑
5-46. A = 720 lb ↑ , B = 1380 lb ↑
5-48. A = 310 lb ↑ , B = 357 lb ↑

CHAPTER 6

6-2.   840 in.^{4}
6-4.   73.1 in.^{4}
6-6.   25.6 in.^{4}
6-8.   321 in.^{4}
6-10. 21.08 in.^{4}
6-12. 1103 in.^{4}
6-14. 351.5 in.^{4}
6-16. 10,052 in.^{4}
6-18. 2944 in.^{4}
6-20. 187.6 in.^{4}
6-22. 137.5 in.^{4}
6-24. 4.52 in.
6-26. 1.23 in.
6-28. 4.44 in.
6-30. 2.98 ft
6-32. 5.24 in.

Index